ARIZONA ROCKS!

A Guide to Geologic Sites in the Grand Canyon State

T. Scott Bryan

2013
Mountain Press Publishing Company
Missoula, Montana

ACKNOWLEDGMENTS

Numerous people contributed their time and knowledge to improve this book with suggestions, corrections, amplifications, and photographs, and I thank them all. Above all was my wife, Betty.

Readers of the full manuscript were Jon Spencer, Senior Geologist, Arizona Geological Survey; John V. Bezy, National Park Service (retired) and author of eight Down-to-Earth books published by the Arizona Geological Survey; and Jennifer Carey, my editor at Mountain Press. A number of personal friends also read and made valuable comments on the entire manuscript, including Carol Beverly, Mike Jacka, Kevin Leany, Karen Lowe, Bob Mabery, Patricia Motter Nies, Paul Strasser, and two who wished to remain anonymous. Readers of specific sections included National Park Service employees Judy Hellmich-Bryan, Max King, Sue Rutman, Kristin Sanderson, and Cecelia Shields.

Some photographs were obtained with the assistance of Arizona State Park employees Ellen Bilbrey and Dave Pawlik, and Arizona Geological Survey geologist Joe Cook. Public domain photos were obtained from the Web sites of several national parks, and from public domain/public license Web sites PDphoto.org, pixabay.com, and Creative Commons. Satellite photos came from the U.S. Geological Survey's Earth Explorer site and the high-resolution relief maps from the Earth Resources Observation and Science Center, also of the U.S. Geological Survey.

Library of Congress Cataloging-in-Publication Data

Bryan, T. Scott.
Arizona rocks! : a guide to geologic sites in the Grand Canyon State / T. Scott Bryan. — First [edition].
    pages cm
Includes bibliographical references and index.
ISBN 978-0-87842-598-3 (pbk. : alk. paper)
1. Geology—Arizona. I. Title.
QE85.B79 2013
557.91—dc23

2012039065

PRINTED IN HONG KONG

MP Mountain Press
PUBLISHING COMPANY
P.O. Box 2399 • Missoula, MT 59806 • 406-728-1900
800-234-5308 • info@mtnpress.com
www.mountain-press.com

PREFACE

People have asked why I would want to live in that "awful, hot desert," as if that was all there is to Arizona. But, of course, the state is not all desert and it's not always hot. Much of Arizona is highlands and studded with forested mountains that reach above 10,000 feet. There are numerous rivers and riparian areas, deep canyons, and young volcanoes. Arizona's spectacular landscape and variety of rocks are the end result of 1.8 billion years of geologic history.

Eleven national parks include canyons and volcanoes, strange rock pinnacles and sinkholes, and a petrified forest. State parks preserve a fabulous limestone cavern, a huge natural bridge, and what looks like an old volcano but isn't. One of the state's many exposures of the Great Unconformity is within a Phoenix city park. Elsewhere are dinosaur trackways, the best-preserved meteorite crater in the world, and the remnants of immense explosive calderas. Indeed, Arizona boasts a geologic diversity that few other states can match.

Following an introduction that summarizes Arizona's statewide geology, this book covers the geology of forty-four special places with short descriptions that make the setting of each site accessible to the casual visitor. An extensive glossary defines technical terms used in the text, and a list of published and online resources will lead interested readers to more detailed information about each place.

All but one of the locations in this book are open to the public; the single exception (Site 19) is closed to entry but still can be viewed closely from public roads. Some of these places are inside the limits of major cities, and others are more remote.

Many are national, state, or other parks where there are entry fees. Some are on Bureau of Land Management and U.S. Forest Service lands. A few places are privately owned but operated as public attractions. All sites are accessible via paved highways or (in just three cases) improved dirt roads where high-clearance vehicles are not necessary. Maps provided with the site descriptions should be all you need to reach them.

A few of these places are on unrestricted public lands where rock and mineral collecting is allowed, and these are described in the text. However, it must be noted that most of these sites are protected places. National and state parks prohibit specimen collecting, as do the several Indian reservations and commercial enterprises encountered here, so please look and enjoy but leave things as you find them.

Several of the locations in this book are within Indian reservations. Access is not restricted so long as a visitor stays on maintained roads. Under no circumstances should a visitor approach an Indian residence unless specifically invited to do so, and the people should not be photographed without permission. Rock and mineral collecting require permits on all reservations.

Unfortunately, it also is necessary to point out that Arizona shares a border with Mexico. Although infrequent, incidents between Americans and illegal immigrants or drug smugglers sometimes take place. Therefore, simple words of warning: when visiting any of the places near the border, if you see people hiking north with few or no belongings and no vehicle in evidence, or especially if they appear to be carrying large, heavy loads, then stay away from them.

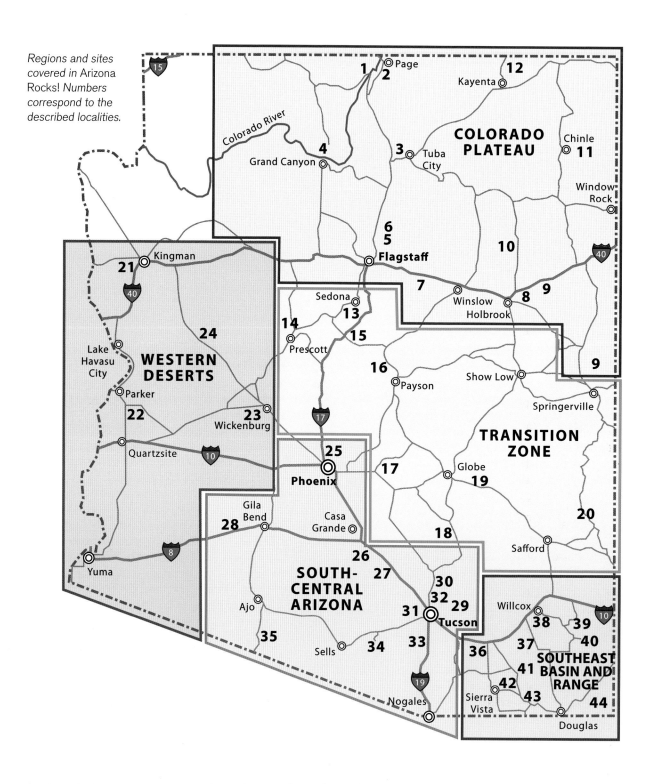

Regions and sites covered in Arizona Rocks! Numbers correspond to the described localities.

1
2 Page
12
Kayenta

Colorado River
4
Grand Canyon
3 Tuba City
COLORADO PLATEAU
Chinle 11
Window Rock

6
5
Flagstaff
10
9

7
Sedona
13
Winslow
8 9
Holbrook

Kingman
21
40
14
15
Prescott

WESTERN DESERTS
24
16 Payson
Show Low
Springerville

Lake Havasu City
Parker

22
23
Wickenburg
17
25
Phoenix
TRANSITION ZONE
Globe
19

Quartzsite
10

Gila Bend
28
Casa Grande
18
Safford
20

8
Yuma
26
27
SOUTH-CENTRAL ARIZONA
30
32 29
Willcox
38
39
40

Ajo
35
34
33
31 Tucson
37
41
SOUTHEAST BASIN AND RANGE
36
42
43
44

Sells
19
Nogales
Sierra Vista
Douglas

15
40
17

CONTENTS

AN INTRODUCTION TO ARIZONA'S GEOLOGY

The Earth has existed for about 4,600,000,000 years—4.6 billion years. It is difficult for anybody, geologists included, to truly understand the scale of geologic time, but time is what allows geologic processes to work. Huge changes take place via small individual events spread out through time. For example, the Grand Canyon is about 5,000 feet deep and has been carved by the Colorado River within the last 5.3 million years. That required the river to cut downward at an average rate of less than one-hundredth of an inch per year! Even so, at that minuscule rate it took just one-thousandth (0.11 percent) of Earth history to create one of the largest canyons on Earth.

At the bottom of the Grand Canyon, the river has exposed rocks nearly 1.8 billion years old, some of the oldest rocks in Arizona. A lot can happen in 1.8 billion years, but the geologic history of Arizona is relatively simple at its basic level. There have been three main episodes of mountain building, called orogenies, separated from one another by long periods of quiet sedimentary rock deposition and erosion. The first episode, called the Yavapai-Mazatzal Orogeny, began in Precambrian time, nearly 1.8 billion years ago. No rocks in Arizona today existed before that time. Over the course of 200 million years, this orogeny created the oldest bedrock in much of the American Southwest, including all of Arizona. The volcanic and sedimentary rocks that were deposited during this time were extensively metamorphosed into gneiss and schist, folded and faulted, and intruded by granitic magmas. This activity created a great new mountain range. Another episode of igneous intrusions formed extensive areas of granite about 1.4 billion years ago. These hard igneous and metamorphic rocks, known to geologists as basement rocks because they usually are below the younger sedimentary and volcanic rocks, are found throughout the state.

What goes up must come down. Erosion carved those mountains away, forming a gentle landscape. Sediments deposited on this surface between 1.2 billion and 800 million years ago were tilted and weakly metamorphosed during a second, relatively small orogeny, sometimes called the Grand Canyon Disturbance. In turn, they eroded down, and in places were completely eroded away, before the end of Precambrian time. This set the stage for a very long span of intermittent sedimentary deposition.

During Paleozoic time, much of Arizona was underwater along a continental shelf. For 300 million years sea level alternately rose and fell. Each cycle resulted in a series of sedimentary rocks being deposited on beaches (sandstone) and in nearshore or shallow water environments (siltstone, shale, and limestone). When sea level fell, the rocks were exposed to weathering. Some sediments were largely untouched, but others were mostly removed by erosion before the next episode of deposition began. These interruptions in deposition form unconformities, or breaks in the rock record. Toward the end of Paleozoic time, the region was sometimes above sea level, and sand dunes formed on the dry, exposed land.

Environments began to change as time moved into the Mesozoic Era. Subduction took place along the west coast of North America as the Pacific Ocean's crust began to slide beneath the western edge of the continent. This new tectonic activity caused much of Arizona to be uplifted slightly above sea level. Sedimentation continued in many parts of the state, but more of it was on dry land rather than in seawater. Several mountain-building episodes affected western North America during this time. In Arizona, the most extensive and most important was the Laramide Orogeny, named after the Laramie Mountains in Wyoming. It began about 80 million years ago and continued in Arizona until 50 million years ago. There was extensive igneous activity and volcanoes formed, some of which produced huge calderas. Many of Arizona's mineral deposits, including most of

GEOLOGIC TIME SCALE
U.S. Geological Survey, 2010

Era	Period	Epoch	Age	Notable Events in Arizona
			present	Clovis Culture; modern cycle of erosion
CENOZOIC	Quaternary	Holocene		
		Pleistocene		
			2.6	earliest of San Francisco Peaks volcanic eruptions
	Tertiary (Neogene)	Pliocene		three modern provinces begin to form
		Miocene		
			23.0	Colorado Plateau uplift, metamorphic core complexes form; numerous caldera volcanoes
	Tertiary (Paleogene)	Oligocene		
		Eocene		
		Paleocene		middle of Laramide Orogeny
			65.5	
MESOZOIC	Cretaceous			Tucson and other caldera-forming volcanoes
	Jurassic		145	extensive sand seas in northern Arizona
	Triassic		200	Petrified Forest and early dinosaurs
			251.0	rim of the Grand Canyon
PALEOZOIC	Permian			Sedona's red rocks
			299	
	Carboniferous	Pennsylvanian		
			318	
		Mississippian		deposition during repeated rises and falls in sea level, separated by erosional unconformities
			359	
	Devonian		416	
	Silurian		444	
	Ordovician		488	
	Cambrian			oldest flat-lying rocks in the Grand Canyon
			542.0	time spanned by the Great Unconformity
PRECAMBRIAN	Proterozoic Eon			oldest rocks in Arizona
			2,500	
	Archean Eon		3,850	
	Hadean Eon			
			4,600	approximate age of Earth

Age in millions of years before present

2

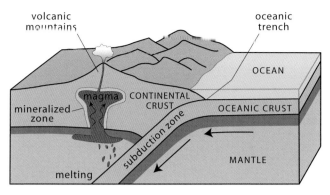

Subduction, which caused the Laramide Orogeny and most other Arizona mountain-building events, takes place when a plate of oceanic crust is forced to slide beneath another plate, usually continental crust. Partial melting of the subducted plate produces magma, which rises to form plutons, volcanoes, and mineral deposits.

The Colorado Plateau Province extends north from the Mogollon Rim (pronounced "muggy-own"). It is relatively flat, with elevations mostly between 5,000 and 7,000 feet above sea level. Tilted slightly upward toward the north, its geologic structures are subdued and surface features are mostly the result of erosion. The rocks consist of late Paleozoic and Mesozoic sediments warped into broad domes and basins, eroded into mesas and buttes, and carved into river canyons. Here and there the plateau is decorated with youthful volcanic fields.

The Transition Zone Province, also called the Central Highlands, crosses the middle of Arizona from northwest to southeast. Its northern boundary is the Mogollon Rim. From there elevations rapidly drop southward, from over 7,000 to less than 2,000 feet above sea level. The rocks here are the same ages as the Precambrian and Paleozoic formations exposed deep

the important copper porphyry deposits, were formed during the Laramide Orogeny. A northwest-to-southeast belt across southern Arizona probably resembled today's Cascade Range of the Pacific Northwest, a hilly terrain studded with large volcanic cones.

When the Laramide Orogeny ended, the Earth's crust underwent numerous adjustments. In doing so it created modern Arizona's three geologic provinces.

ARIZONA'S GEOLOGIC PROVINCES

Arizona is divided into three geologic provinces—Colorado Plateau, Transition Zone, and Basin and Range. This landscape is a geologically recent development, dating to within the last 30 million years or so. Before then, for example, the Colorado Plateau was near sea level. Now it is the overall highest portion of the state. Exactly how this uplift took place is a matter of some controversy—several theories have been put forward but none has been proved correct to the satisfaction of all geologists. This uplift of the Colorado Plateau occurred at the same time as the development of Arizona's Transition Zone and Basin and Range provinces, and the last uplift of the Rocky Mountains to the east and northeast of Arizona.

Arizona's three geologic provinces

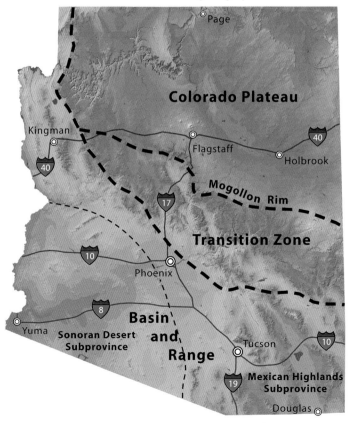

The top of the escarpment of the Mogollon Rim serves as the geologic boundary between the Colorado Plateau (left) and the Transition Zone (right) provinces. —Photo by Doug Dolde, Wikimedia Commons

within the Grand Canyon but which mostly lie hidden at depth on the Colorado Plateau. Geological structures are complex and include faults of the basin-and-range type, making this the most rugged part of Arizona.

The Basin and Range Province crosses southern Arizona. This region was compressed into large-scale folds and thrust faults during the Laramide Orogeny, then stretched by detachment and normal faulting following the orogeny. This final mountain-building action is sometimes referred to as the Basin-and-Range Disturbance. The alternating basin-and-range (valley-and-mountain) structure is most clear in the southeastern part of the state, where elevations range between 2,000 and 5,000 feet with occasional higher peaks; this portion of the province is sometimes referred to as the Mexican Highlands Subprovince. The terrain is subdued and the elevations drop to near sea level in southwestern Arizona, which has been called the Sonoran Desert Subprovince.

DETACHMENT FAULTING AND METAMORPHIC CORE COMPLEXES

The concept of a metamorphic core complex with associated detachment faulting is relatively new to geology, developed in and since the 1970s. We now know that it is a common process in areas where the Earth's crust undergoes large-scale extension, or stretching. Arizona's Basin and Range Province is one of these regions.

The story began around 70 million years ago, during the Laramide Orogeny. Huge quantities of igneous rock were produced. Most formed the granitic intrusions, called plutons, exposed in today's mountains. After the mountain building came to an end, the crust began to stretch. Rocks near the Earth's surface were brittle and broke into individual fault blocks that pulled apart from one another. At the same time, rocks deep below the surface responded in a plastic fashion, deforming

The spectacular Salt River Canyon, on US 60 between Globe and Show Low, is part of Arizona's Transition Zone. Most of the rocks within the canyon are members of the Apache Group and Troy Quartzite, Precambrian rocks equivalent in age to the Grand Canyon Supergroup.

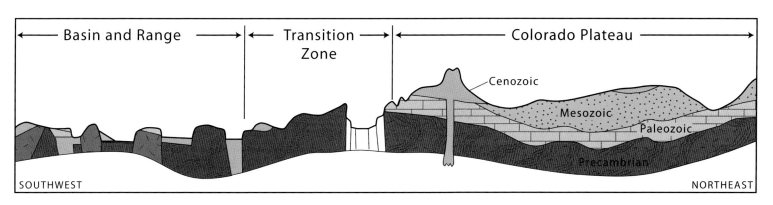

A generalized southwest-to-northeast cross-section of Arizona's geologic provinces. —Modified from Peirce, 1969

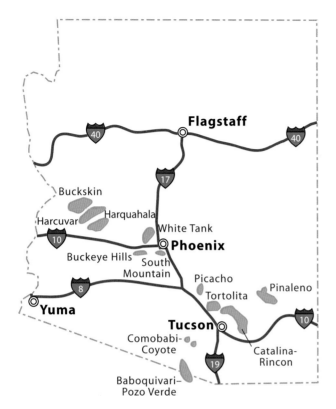

The metamorphic core complexes of Arizona mostly lie along a northwest-to-southeast alignment near the boundary between the Transition Zone and the Basin and Range geologic provinces.

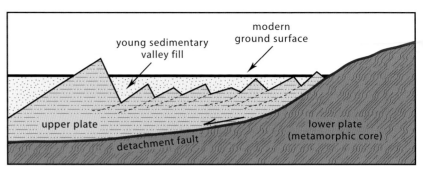

Metamorphic core complexes are exposed when overlying rocks are moved by detachment faulting. —Modified from Drewes, 1977

and flowing like a thick, gooey substance and becoming metamorphic rock such as gneiss. These deformed rocks form the metamorphic core complex of the mountains. Geologists have identified numerous nearly horizontal faults, called detachment faults, that place broken rocks above gneiss and other metamorphic materials. The metamorphic rocks below the fault, sometimes referred to as the lower plate, were uplifted and exposed as the rocks above the fault, the upper plate, were removed by fault movements. In many cases the rocks of the upper plate are completely gone, either eroded away or buried beneath young valley-fill alluvium. The erosion-resistant metamorphic cores form modern mountain masses.

VOLCANIC ACTIVITY

Arizona is an intensely volcanic region, with numerous volcanoes in each of the geologic provinces. Eruptions have taken place in several dozen places during the past 35 million years. Some fields are still active.

Most of the world's volcanoes erupt silica-poor basaltic magma with reasonably quiet, nonexplosive eruptions. The resulting mountains are cinder cones and shield volcanoes often associated with extensive lava flows. In many Arizona cases, these volcanic fields consist of just one or two eroded volcanoes, and sometimes only the lava flows remain. On the other hand, the largest of these fields contain several hundred individual volcanoes and cover areas of several hundred square miles. Arizona's youngest volcano, Sunset Crater Volcano, is in one of these large volcanic fields.

Volcanoes that erupt silica-rich rhyolite magma tend to be more violent, with a single eruption often producing a large caldera, a single volcanic crater miles across. The surrounding countryside is usually buried beneath hundreds of feet of ash and welded tuff. In Arizona, eruptions of this sort have occurred during four known episodes: first during the Yavapai-Mazatzal Orogeny nearly 1.8 billion years ago, another around 160 million years ago, then during the Laramide Orogeny between 80 and 50 million years ago, and finally during the basin-and-range extension and core complex development from 30 to 15 million years ago.

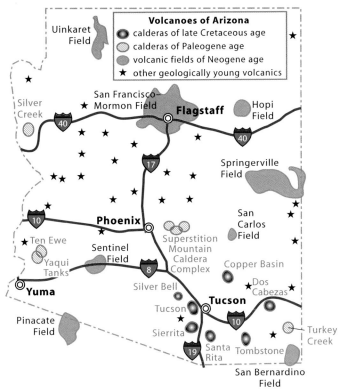

The volcanoes of Arizona

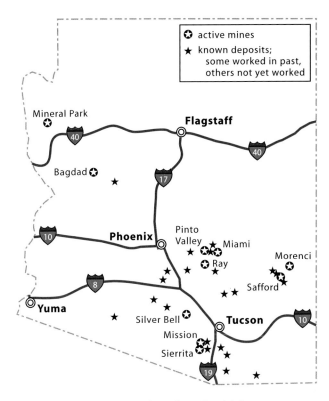

The copper porphyry deposits of Arizona

MINERAL DEPOSITS

Much of Arizona's human history has to do with mining. The early focus was on silver. Mines in southern Arizona were worked by Spanish padres as early as the 1500s, and later discoveries led to boomtowns such as Crown King, Superior, Globe, and Tombstone. Most important, though, has been and still is copper. Excellent displays of Arizona minerals can be seen in the University of Arizona Mineral Museum at the university's Flandrau Science Center in Tucson.

During the Laramide Orogeny, many igneous intrusions formed copper porphyry deposits. A porphyry is an igneous rock that contains distinct mineral crystals disseminated throughout the rock. In a copper porphyry, small amounts of copper minerals also crystallized as part of the granite. At the same time, solutions driven off the cooling magma formed vein deposits in the rock surrounding the intrusion. These were rich enough to support underground mines and boomtowns during the late 1800s and early 1900s. Within the porphyry deposit the ore grade is very low. The copper content of the rock may be less than one-half of one percent (0.5 percent), and the particles of copper minerals are microscopic in size. Taken together the ore is present in huge volumes, entire mountain masses amounting to hundreds of millions, even billions of tons.

With thirty-two known copper porphyry deposits, Arizona is the number one copper producer of the United States. During 2010, Arizona's active copper properties yielded nearly 1.6 billion pounds of copper plus significant amounts of the metals molybdenum, silver, gold, and rhenium (very rare in nature). All of the modern mining is in open pit operations. Most of the companies maintain public viewpoints overlooking the pits. Tours are available at the Mineral Discovery Center and Mission Mine near Tucson, and by reservation at the Bagdad and Morenci mines.

A 99.99 percent pure copper cathode from the smelter at Hayden, Arizona, is on display in the Mineral Discovery Center at Mission Mine.

This chunk of copper ore is on display at the Mineral Discovery Center at Mission Mine.

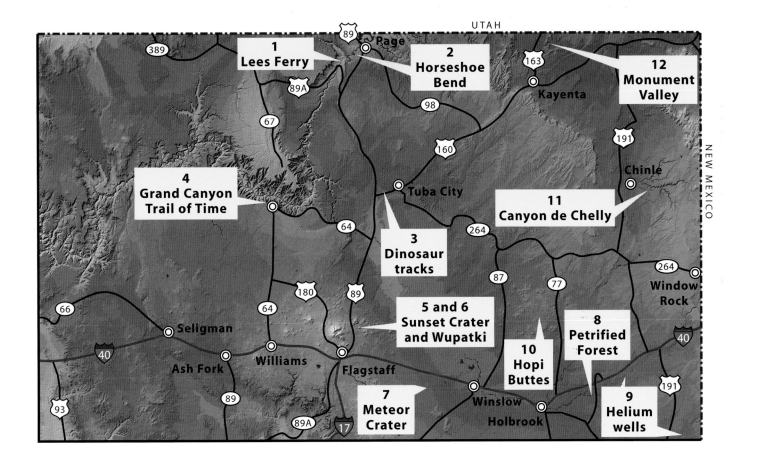

COLORADO PLATEAU PROVINCE

The Colorado Plateau is a huge geologic province, encompassing much of northern Arizona plus portions of New Mexico, Utah, and Colorado. It is a highland region, too. Elevations along its southern edge at the Mogollon Rim are often higher than 7,000 feet above sea level; few places have elevations lower than 4,000 feet, and some mountain summits reach over 10,000 feet. Most of the rock is sedimentary, capped by volcanic materials in a few areas.

Much of the Colorado Plateau is within the Navajo Reservation, the largest Indian reservation in the United States. It covers 16.2 million acres (over 25,000 square miles) and has a population of about 200,000. The smaller Hopi Reservation is surrounded by the Navajo, and nearby are reservations for the Zuni, Mountain Ute, Southern Paiute, and other tribal groups. Visitors are free to travel the roads and take scenic photos on these reservations, but they must recognize tribal laws and customs.

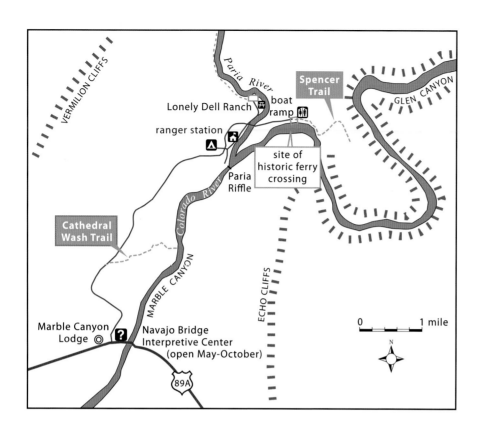

 ## 1. Lees Ferry
A Human and Geological Crossroad

Until the modern construction of bridges and dams, Lees Ferry was the only place a person could safely cross the Colorado River in more than 700 river miles. The human crossing here was made possible because of the soft, easily eroded nature of rocks that allow direct access to the river. Geologically, Lees Ferry is the midpoint in the many layers of sedimentary rock that make up the Colorado Plateau, and its rocks mark a transitional time from shallow oceans to forested shorelines and streams, sandy deserts, and shallow lakes. A spectacular overview of this geology is visible from the Spencer Trail, a strenuous hike made easier by the wonderful geology along the way.

The soft rocks at Lees Ferry are the Moenkopi and Chinle formations. These mostly fine-grained rocks were deposited as silt, clay, and volcanic ash in tidal flats, shallow lakes, and floodplains during Triassic time, between 250 and 200 million years ago. The balanced rocks along the access road from US 89A are made of Shinarump Conglomerate (the lowest member of the Chinle Formation) supported by sandstone pillars of the Moenkopi Formation. The Moenkopi also forms the river shore at the modern boat ramp, while the Chinle occupies the hills behind the nearby historic buildings.

Downstream, exposed below the small rapids of Paria Riffle, are the hard, erosion-resistant, canyon-making Paleozoic rocks of the Grand Canyon Series, the sedimentary rocks that make up the walls of the Grand Canyon. The uppermost of these, forming the rim of the river's gorge everywhere from here through Marble Canyon to the Grand Canyon many miles away, are the Toroweap Formation and Kaibab Limestone of Permian age. These are the rocks in the canyon directly beneath Navajo Bridge on US 89A. They are better seen along Cathedral Wash, a 1.5-mile hike from the Lees Ferry access road through a slot canyon to the river.

Above the boat ramp area, upstream in Glen Canyon and forming the towering Echo and Vermilion cliffs, are Mesozoic rocks. The Moenave, Kayenta, and Navajo formations of Jurassic age are all sandstones, formed along streams and as dunes in Sahara-like sand seas. These are the rocks climbed by the Spencer Trail, accessed from the boat ramp.

The Vermilion Cliffs above Lees Ferry are composed of (from bottom to top) the pinkish Moenkopi, bluish gray Chinle (with finely layered Shinarump Conglomerate at its base), red Moenave, purplish Kayenta, and tan Navajo formations.

Boulders of Shinarump Conglomerate are perched atop pedestals of Moenkopi Formation along the entrance road to Lees Ferry.

The Kaibab Limestone, the uppermost formation of the Grand Canyon Series, forms a sloping platform just downstream from Lees Ferry, where river rafts begin the trip through the Grand Canyon.

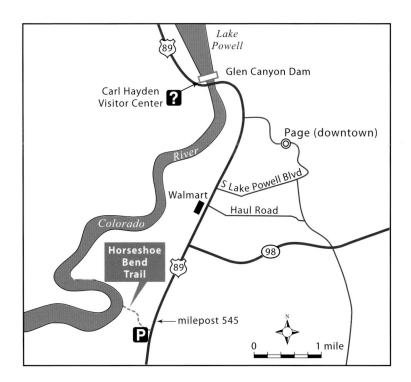

5 million years ago, the stream was trapped in its existing bed. The increase in gradient caused a sudden increase in erosion, and the river cut rapidly and deeply into the sandstone. Now the Colorado River sweeps around a full 270-degree curve as it flows through the entrenched meander called Horseshoe Bend.

The view is spectacular, but be very careful as you near the end of the 0.75-mile trail to the canyon rim. There is no guardrail, and the sheer drop into the canyon is 1,000 feet deep.

Horseshoe Bend, Arizona, in Glen Canyon National Recreation Area, as seen from the lookout point. —Photo by LoggaWiggler, Pixabay Public Domain Images

2. Glen Canyon National Recreation Area
Entrenched Meander at Horseshoe Bend

During much of Jurassic time, northern Arizona was part of a great sea of sand, much like the modern Sahara Desert. Sand dunes piled on top of sand dunes, and eventually they were cemented into a solid sandstone layer as much as 2,000 feet thick. Called the Navajo Sandstone, the rock makes up the bare red rock exposures over much of the Colorado Plateau. You can see the sweeping form of crossbedding in the ancient windblown dunes. Thousands of feet of younger sedimentary formations were laid down on top of the Navajo. Most of those rocks were softer than the solid sandstone. Although they can be seen to the north in Utah, here they were eroded away long ago.

In Pliocene time, the ancient Colorado River swung back and forth in a sinuous fashion, meandering across a gentle landscape. Then as the Colorado Plateau was uplifted about

3. Tuba City Dinosaur Tracks
Where Giants Once Walked

Dinosaur tracks are not particularly rare, but the ones near Tuba City are the most accessible of any in Arizona. The tracks are within the Moenave Formation, fine-grained sandstone deposited along streams just over 200 million years ago, either very late in Triassic time or early in Jurassic time.

The tracks are trace fossils—evidence of an animal's presence without actual fossilized remains. They are classified on the basis of size and shape without knowing for certain what animals created them. Based on their age, their large three-toed size, and that they were made by animals that walked on two legs, these tracks were made by carnivorous dinosaurs called theropods. Some people have equated them to such known species as *Dilophosaurus* (fictionalized as the venom-spitting dinosaur in the *Jurassic Park* movie) and *Coelophysis* (herd-forming, ostrichlike dinosaurs), but we will never really know. All we have are the tracks, trace fossil genera that include *Eubrontes*, *Grallator*, and *Kayentapus*. These are definitely not tracks of *Tyrannosaurus rex*—that famous beast did not live until late in Cretaceous time, 135 million years after these tracks were made. The variety in tracks makes it likely that several different kinds of dinosaurs were present. Smaller footprints in the area might relate to early crocodilians or even to our own distant ancestors, the mammal-like reptiles. Small, round or irregular masses present in the sandstone are concretions, areas hardened by durable minerals deposited by groundwater after the sandstone formed. They are not dinosaur eggs or dung!

These trackways are on the Navajo Indian Reservation, and often local residents are present to act as guides for a small fee. They may point out a "claw," which some geologists think is most likely part of a fish. If no guides are present, feel free to explore the area on your own.

Dinosaur tracks with a U.S. quarter for scale. The smaller track could be the forefoot of the animal that made the larger track, or it could be from a different animal.

Dinosaur tracks are exposed along the road to the village of Moenave west of Tuba City.

Moenave

Tuba City

89

Tuba City dinosaur trackways

160

Moenkopi 264

160

N

0   5 miles

4. Grand Canyon National Park
On the Trail of Time

The scale of the Grand Canyon is difficult to fully envision and appreciate. It is 282 miles long and about 5,000 feet deep, and nearly 2 billion years of Earth history is revealed by the rocks within the canyon. There are, to be sure, many gaps in that geologic record. Called unconformities, they represent time spans when erosion rather than deposition took place. To some extent, the canyon is like a book missing some pages.

The Grand Canyon's rock record begins far back in Precambrian time with igneous and metamorphic rocks. The Vishnu Schist, Elves Chasm Gneiss, Zoroaster Granite, and other basement rocks are almost 1.8 billion years old. They formed during a huge mountain-building episode called the Yavapai-Mazatzal Orogeny. Those mountains were eroded to a flat platform upon which were deposited younger Precambrian rocks starting 1.2 billion years ago. These younger rocks are known as the Grand Canyon Supergroup.

Another episode of mountain building uplifted and tilted all those old rocks, and erosion again planed the terrain to a flat, depositional surface before the end of Precambrian time. The next sequence of rocks was deposited throughout the Paleozoic Era, starting 525 million years ago with the Tapeats Sandstone of Cambrian age at the bottom and ending 270 million years ago with the Kaibab Limestone of Permian age at the top. Between those two are numerous other rock formations and several unconformities. These Grand Canyon Series rocks remain nearly flat-lying and make up most of the canyon walls.

The canyon views are spectacular, but for most visitors the geology is literally out of reach, down the rugged trails deep within the canyon. The park solved this problem with its easy Trail of Time, which starts at the Yavapai Geology Museum and extends back in time to end at Verkamp's Visitor Center at the east end of Grand Canyon Village. (Of course, you can walk

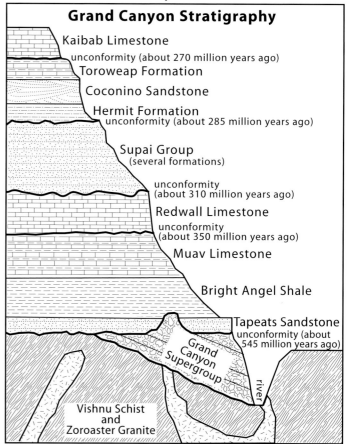

You can see these rock formations and unconformities in the Grand Canyon.

Grand Canyon Stratigraphy

Kaibab Limestone
unconformity (about 270 million years ago)
Toroweap Formation
Coconino Sandstone
Hermit Formation
unconformity (about 285 million years ago)
Supai Group
(several formations)
unconformity
(about 310 million years ago)
Redwall Limestone
unconformity
(about 350 million years ago)
Muav Limestone
Bright Angel Shale
Tapeats Sandstone
unconformity (about 545 million years ago)
Grand Canyon Supergroup
river
Vishnu Schist and Zoroaster Granite

the other direction, up through time, if you wish.) Part of the popular South Rim Trail, it is 2,000 meters long so that every 1 meter—one long stride—represents 1 million years of time. Every 10 meters along the way are brass time-line plates embedded in the walkway. Interpretive signs, sighting tubes, and forty-six limestone pedestals topped with large specimens of rock are located along the time line at the places corresponding to each formation's age. The 1 million years nearest the Yavapai Museum is expanded into a scale of human perspective.

A column (center right), showing the layers of rock in the Grand Canyon, is made out of samples of the actual rocks and marks the start of the Trail of Time. —Photo by Michael Quinn, National Park Service

The Grand Canyon from Yaki Point —National Park Service

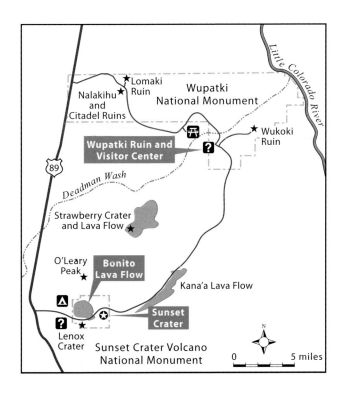

5. Sunset Crater Volcano National Monument
Arizona's Youngest Volcano

The San Francisco Volcanic Field is the largest in Arizona, covering an area of about 2,000 square miles. The earliest of its eruptions took place 6 million years ago. The youngest members of the field are Sunset Crater Volcano and some lava flows and smaller, nearby craters that formed less than 1,000 years ago.

Exactly when Sunset Crater erupted is unclear. The oft-stated date of AD 1064 is now believed inaccurate, though the activity did take place between AD 1040 and AD 1100. Rising just over 1,000 feet above the surrounding plateau, Sunset Crater Volcano is one of the largest cinder cones on Earth. It formed start-to-finish during a single eruptive episode that probably lasted only a few months at most. Near the end of the eruption, the Bonito and Kana'a lava flows erupted from vents near the base of the cone. Vents near the top of the volcano released steam that oxidized iron in the cinders into the reddish orange color that gave the mountain its name.

To protect the fragile slopes, visitors are not allowed to climb Sunset Crater. A trail climbs to the top of the smaller, nearby Lenox Crater.

Sunset Crater Volcano erupted a little less than 1,000 years ago.

The Bonito Lava Flow formed near the end of Sunset Crater Volcano's eruption. O'Leary Peak in the background is a volcano much older and larger than Sunset Crater.

6. Wupatki National Monument
Prehistoric Agriculture in the Ashes

Sinagua Indians, among the direct ancestors of today's Hopi, Zuni, and other local tribes, had been living in the vicinity of Flagstaff, Arizona, for at least four hundred years before their lives were disrupted by the eruption of Sunset Crater Volcano about 1,000 years ago. We know they witnessed the eruption because molds of corn cobs that had to have been intentionally placed into the still-molten lava have been found in the Bonito flow. Although the people moved away from the area for several decades, when they returned it was to Wupatki, a fascinating place whose archaeology and scenery are based on geology.

Sunset Crater's eruption blanketed the desert to its north with volcanic ash and cinders. The Sinagua, whose name means "without water" in Spanish, were experts at farming without irrigation, but it seems likely that the Wupatki area was too dry to support any agriculture before the eruption. Perhaps the ash acted as mulch and retained enough rainwater to temporarily

The rich red Moenkopi Formation capped by lava flows between Sunset Crater Volcano and Wupatki national monuments.

allow corn and melon crops in the previously uninhabitable area. In any case, the Sinagua began to move back into the area by AD 1100, and at least one thousand people occupied the area of Wupatki National Monument by AD 1130. These hospitable conditions did not last long, and Wupatki was abandoned before AD 1250.

The rich red sandstone that makes up the bluffs is the Moenkopi Formation of early Triassic age. Below the Moenkopi is the Permian-age Kaibab Limestone, exposed only in a few places by deep erosion. Above the Moenkopi are some recent stream gravels, and the volcano's ash and cinders. Because the pueblos were built using Moenkopi sandstone, they often blend into and seem part of the landscape.

Adjacent to the monument's visitor center is Wupatki Pueblo, with one hundred rooms—by far the largest of the pueblos in the national monument. While it was home to many people, it was also a ceremonial center. The site includes a large amphitheater, a ball court, and most notably a blowhole, a hole in the ground through which the wind blows in or out depending on the outside atmospheric pressure. The air flows through a fissure in the Moenkopi Formation that no doubt connects to a cavern of some size within the Kaibab Limestone below. Blowholes such as this are sacred to modern Pueblo Indians—to the Hopi the air movement is driven by *Yaapontsa*, the wind spirit. This blowhole was probably sacred to the Sinagua, too, and it may be why the large development of Wupatki Pueblo was located here.

A rock vault and screen protect the blowhole at Wupatki. A strong breeze blowing out of the blowhole is lifting the author's hat.

Wupatki Pueblo is made from sandstone of the Moenkopi Formation, outcropping in the distance in this photo.

7. Barringer Meteorite Crater
The Best-Preserved Impact Crater on Earth

Commonly known simply as Meteor Crater, the Barringer Meteorite Crater is 4,100 feet across and 570 feet deep. A rim surrounding the crater rises 100 to 200 feet above the flat plateau and is composed of jumbled rock fragments ranging from particles as small as 1 micron to boulders as big as houses. The crater formed when the Canyon Diablo Meteor struck the Earth 49,300 years ago at a speed of 28,000 miles per hour. The blast was at least equivalent to a 2.5 megaton bomb.

The origin of Meteor Crater was controversial for many years. In 1891, G. K. Gilbert, the director of the U.S. Geological Survey, "proved" a volcanic origin for the crater and stated that the meteorites found around the crater were there by coincidence. Geologist D. M. Barringer felt otherwise. In 1902, he established the Standard Iron Company to mine the iron-nickel meteorite that he thought would be buried in the crater, although as it turned out it was mostly vaporized on impact. Barringer set about trying to convince other scientists of the astronomical origin of the crater. Most remained skeptical, and it wasn't until 1963 that a publication by astrogeologist Eugene M. Shoemaker convinced people that a meteor blasted out the crater.

Shoemaker presented two main pieces of evidence. First, the rim around the crater is composed of the same rock formations that underlie the surrounding Colorado Plateau, *except* that they are in reverse order—broken fragments of older formations lie on top of younger rocks. This could only happen if a shockwave shattered, uplifted, and overturned the rocks. Second, coesite and stishovite were found in the sandstone blasted by the impact. Those minerals are pure silicon dioxide, like quartz,

The rocks around the rim of Barringer Meteorite Crater were turned upward and shattered by the impact that formed the crater.

but they are denser and form only under pressures greater than 300,000 pounds per square inch. Neither the overturned rocks nor the dense minerals can be produced by a volcano.

The size of the original meteor remains a question. The Lunar and Planetary Institute estimates that it was between 30 and 150 feet in diameter and weighed anywhere from 50,000 to 300,000 tons. The impact vaporized much of the meteor. The remainder was shattered into billions of pieces and spread out over more than 70 square miles. Only 30 tons of fragments have been collected.

Barringer Meteorite Crater is privately owned, and an admission charge gives access to a museum, interpretive viewpoints, and trails.

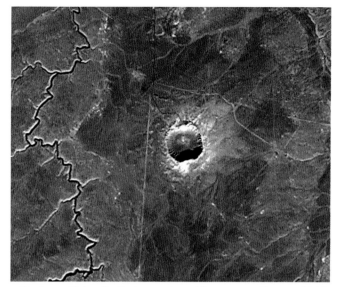

Barringer Meteorite Crater as viewed from space. Canyon Diablo winds through the left side of the image. —Landsat 5 satellite image, Earth Explorer program, U.S. Geological Survey

It is difficult to judge the scale of Barringer Meteorite Crater when viewed from the visitor center.

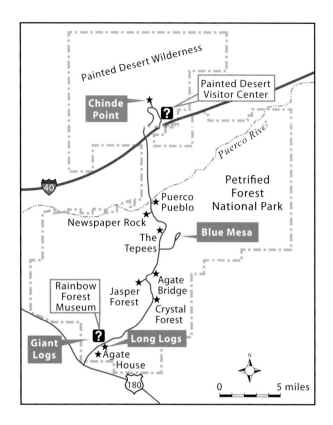

The Petrified Forest was set aside as a national park because of its tremendous concentration of fossilized logs. At least fourteen species of petrified trees have been found in the park. Most have been identified as *Araucarioxylon arizonicum* (Arizona's official state fossil), a plant related to the Norfolk Island pine, monkey-puzzle, and South American araucaria trees of today. Fossil fronds, pollen, and spores of over two hundred other species of plants have also been found.

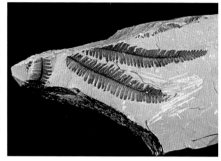

Phlebopteris (Laccopteris) smithii, a fossil fern found in the Chinle Formation.
—National Park Service

You can still see the tree rings in this petrified log.

8. Petrified Forest National Park
Remnants of a Flourishing Ecosystem

Early in Triassic time, about 220 million years ago, this area was an open valley crossed by meandering streams. In highlands to the west and southwest, a wide variety of animals lived in a lush tropical forest of gymnosperms, ferns, cycads, and horsetails. Large rivers washed from the mountains, and the debris they carried was deposited on the floodplain. Volcanic ash accumulated as well and provided the silica that eventually replaced the plant and animal remains, preserving them as fossils. The nearly 2,000 feet of fossiliferous sediment is now the Chinle Formation.

Preserved animals are of great interest, too, with over sixty species identified. Of most interest are archosaurs, the category of reptiles that includes dinosaurs, crocodiles, and the forerunners of birds. The streams contained amphibians, freshwater sharks and lungfish, and clams and snails. Borings preserved in the petrified logs show that insects such as termites, beetles, and cockroaches were there, too.

New fossils are frequently found. Should you find one when exploring the park, please leave it untouched and notify a park ranger so that it can be properly added to the paleontological treasure trove. Collecting the petrified wood and other fossils inside the national park is illegal, and the law is strictly enforced.

Between the Painted Desert Visitor Center at the north entrance and the Rainbow Forest Museum near the south entrance are numerous viewpoints and trails. Places like Chinde Point near the north entrance overlook the colorful Painted Desert. The Tepees and Blue Mesa areas give close-up looks at the eroding Chinle Formation. Some of the best examples of petrified wood are along the Crystal Forest nature trail, while Long Logs, Giant Logs, and Jasper Forest host additional examples.

Colorful petrified wood litters the slopes along the Crystal Forest Trail.

Rapid erosion of the soft claystone of the Chinle Formation has formed badland topography at Blue Mesa.

The Chinle Formation of the Painted Desert is colored by trace amounts of iron oxide minerals within the soft claystone. This view is from Tiponi Point.

9. Pinta Dome and St. Johns Helium Fields
A Critical Supply of Rare Gas

Helium, an inert gas, is produced very slowly by the radioactive decay of uranium in rocks. Nearly all helium on Earth is the result of that decay over the 4.6 billion years of the planet's history. Helium migrates up through cracks in the overlying rock until it either escapes into the atmosphere or is trapped. An impermeable layer folded up into a dome, such as the Pinta Dome just east of Petrified Forest National Park, makes a good trap. Helium cannot be synthesized, and it is very expensive to extract helium from the atmosphere. Another inert gas, argon, can replace helium in some uses, but helium remains critical for many modern applications, such as the supercooling fluid in medical magnetic resonance imaging machines and other low-temperature processes, the production of optical fibers, leak detection in ultrahigh pressure systems, the coolant in some nuclear reactors, and the manufacture of LCD flat-panel television screens. Probably the one use most people think of—helium as the lifting gas in blimps and party balloons—is not critical and is growing controversial as the supply of helium dwindles.

Until 1996, the U.S. government purchased helium as a by-product of natural gas production, and it was stored in sedimentary domes in the Great Plains. In 1996 Congress passed a bill requiring the federal helium reserve to be sold by 2015. In the interim, consumption of the gas has skyrocketed. What remains in storage is administered by the Bureau of Land Management, which sells the gas at what some authorities claim to be an unrealistically low price. Although some helium is still recovered by natural gas producers, that production is far less than the demand. In July 2012 the Committee on Natural Resources in the U.S. House of Representatives began hearings to address this shortage by reestablishing a strategic helium reserve and encouraging domestic production.

Future production at the Pinta Dome is only slightly possible because most of its gas was pumped out between 1961 and 1976. Potentially more important is the St. Johns–Springerville Gas Field on the Arizona–New Mexico border, which is said to be the largest undeveloped gas field in the United States. Without new production, helium will grow increasingly rare. Some forecasts say that by the year 2100, the helium for a party balloon could cost hundreds of dollars.

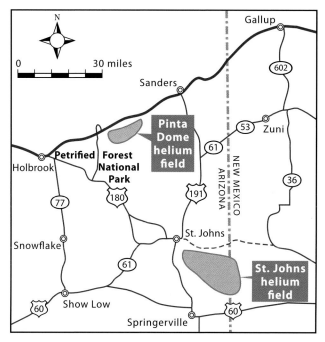

The dark ridge of Pinta Dome on the skyline viewed from Blue Mesa in Petrified Forest National Park.

10. Hopi Buttes Volcanic Field
A Landscape from Steam-Driven Explosions

Formed between 8.5 and 6 million years ago, the Hopi Buttes (*Tsezhin Bi'i* in Navajo) are volcanoes of a very different sort. The eruptions were violent, yet they did not form typical volcanic cones. The Hopi Buttes formed when rising magma encountered the saturated lakebeds of the Bidahochi Formation, causing water to flash into steam. Steam-driven explosions blew out cone-shaped vents, called diatremes, topped by shallow, circular craters, called maars. Magma flowed into the diatremes and partially filled the maars. The lava was later buried by younger lakebeds. Now erosion has stripped away many softer deposits, revealing the diatremes as buttes of resistant volcanic rock as much as several hundred feet high.

Most of the three hundred or so Hopi Buttes lie within the Navajo and Hopi Indian reservations. Extensive explorations require tribal permits, but casual investigations do not. AZ 77 passes between the diatremes called the Five Buttes. The maar at Coliseum Diatreme, a bit more than 4 miles west of AZ 77 near Indian Wells, resembles an ancient Roman arena and can be entered. The Morale Claim produced uranium from the sediment deposited within the maar of Red Clay Mesa, and a complete cross-section of a diatreme and maar is visible from AZ 77 at Deshgish Butte.

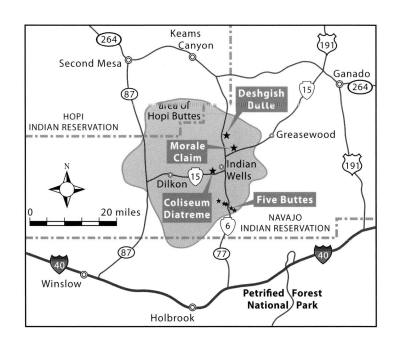

AZ 77 passes through the Five Buttes. View to the north.

The Hopi Buttes Volcanic Field from the air. AZ 77 from Holbrook to Indian Wells passes between the Five Buttes (bottom right).
—U.S. Geological Survey

This unnamed Hopi Butte is near Bidahochi.

The light-colored rocks are lake deposits of the Coliseum maar crater, viewed from Indian Route 15.

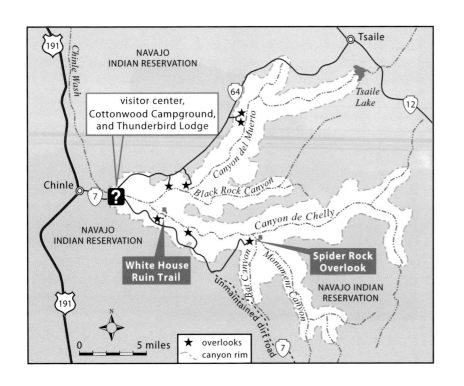

11. Canyon de Chelly National Monument
The Spectacular Navajo Heartland

After the U.S. government forced the Navajo away from their homeland in the Long Walk of 1864, Canyon de Chelly was the first place they returned to in 1868. We pronounce *de Chelly* as "d'-shay." It probably should be closer to "tsay-yee" because the name originated as a Spanish aberration of the Navajo *Tseyi*, meaning "place within the rocks." Most of the rock exposed in Canyon de Chelly is the same as that in the buttes at Monument Valley (Site 12). Dating to Permian time, Organ Rock Shale forms the canyon floors. It is visible in a few places, perhaps most obviously at the base of Spider Rock. Above the shale is De Chelly Sandstone, the well-cemented sand dunes that form the canyon walls. Along the rim of the canyons and forming the very top of Spider Rock is Shinarump Conglomerate, the erosion-resistant bottom member of the

Canyon de Chelly from Tseyi Overlook. —National Park Service

28

Spider Rock, towering above Canyon de Chelly, is mostly De Chelly Sandstone, capped by Shinarump Conglomerate and resting on Organ Rock Shale. —Photo by Nikater, Wikimedia Commons

Chinle Formation. Note that the Moenkopi Formation, which lies between the De Chelly and the Shinarump in Monument Valley, is missing here.

These canyons have been occupied almost continuously for at least 7,000 years. The all-but-impermeable Organ Rock Shale made this possible. Rainwater that falls on the plateau moves easily through the porous De Chelly Sandstone, but when it reaches the shale, it is forced to flow laterally, emerging as springs near the canyon floor. The perennial stream allows year-round agriculture even in times of drought. Erosion of the sandstone at the base of the cliffs, weakened by groundwater flow at the sandstone-shale contact, formed the alcoves occupied by ancient cliff dwellings.

Although administered by the National Park Service, Canyon de Chelly National Monument is entirely owned and managed by Navajo Indians. About seventy families live and farm in the canyons, and entrance is allowed only with a guide. The roads and viewpoints along the canyon rims are open to the general public, as is the trail from the south rim to the White House Pueblo Ruin. Although strenuous, the round-trip hike of 2.5 miles is the best way to experience the geology of Canyon de Chelly.

12. Monument Valley
Monolithic Sandstone Buttes

To the Navajo Indians, Monument Valley is *Tse'Bii'Ndzisgaii*, the "valley of rocks." Here, the sandstone buttes and mesas stand as high as 1,000 feet above the surrounding valley floor, where there are smaller rock formations and extensive sand dunes. The flat-lying rocks all date to the Permian and Triassic periods of geologic time. Each unit was eroded for a while before the next unit was deposited on top of it. From top to bottom, the very tallest buttes and mesas are capped with Shinarump Conglomerate, the bottom member of the Chinle Formation. This hard, erosion-resistant rock helps preserve the buttes. Next is Moenkopi Formation, hardly visible as thin slopes between the Shinarump and the vertical cliffs of crossbedded De Chelly Sandstone, which formed from ancient sand dunes. The valley floor and the bases of the buttes are Organ Rock Shale. Easily eroded, it barely supports the monoliths. Slabs of the sandstone sometimes separate along joints and fall when the soft shale is worn away. In this way, mesas become buttes, and buttes become pinnacles. Very soon, geologically speaking, Monument Valley's monuments will be gone.

Monument Valley Navajo Tribal Park is a fee area open to the general public. Visitors can take the 17-mile loop of Valley Drive without a guide. The dirt road is rough, but you do not need four-wheel drive or a high-clearance vehicle. The Wildcat Trail around West Mitten Butte can be hiked without a guide, too. Trips to archaeological sites and other features not accessible to the unguided public are available with Navajo guides who can be hired at the visitor center.

The Mittens and Merrick Butte beyond Valley Drive in Monument Valley. —Photo by FF23-fr, Creative Commons

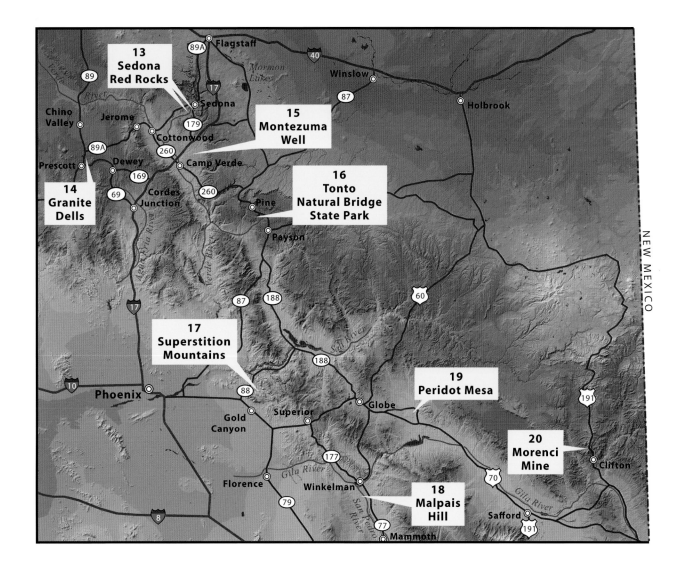

The map shows the following labeled locations:

- **13 Sedona Red Rocks**
- **14 Granite Dells**
- **15 Montezuma Well**
- **16 Tonto Natural Bridge State Park**
- **17 Superstition Mountains**
- **18 Malpais Hill**
- **19 Peridot Mesa**
- **20 Morenci Mine**

Cities and towns: Flagstaff, Winslow, Holbrook, Chino Valley, Jerome, Sedona, Cottonwood, Prescott, Dewey, Camp Verde, Cordes Junction, Pine, Payson, Phoenix, Gold Canyon, Superior, Globe, Florence, Winkelman, Mammoth, Safford, Clifton

NEW MEXICO

TRANSITION ZONE PROVINCE

The Transition Zone lies both geologically and geographically between the Colorado Plateau and the Basin and Range provinces. Its rocks are mostly the same as those on the Colorado Plateau and, as there, are nearly flat-lying. Before and during the Laramide Orogeny, the Transition Zone was uplifted into mountains called the Mogollon Highlands. Some rocks as high as 7,000 feet in elevation along the Mogollon Rim, the escarpment that separates the province from the Colorado Plateau, are equivalent to formations deep within the Grand Canyon. When the Laramide Orogeny ended, some of the region broke apart in a fashion similar to the Basin and Range. With features in common with the surrounding provinces, the Transition Zone is the most rugged part of Arizona.

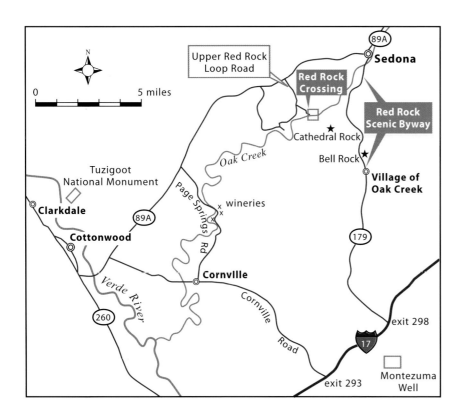

13. Sedona's Red Rock Cliffs
Remnants of a Rising Sea

Towering cliffs of rich red Schnebly Hill Formation, a mixed sequence of sandstone, siltstone, and limestone, surround Sedona. The Hermit Formation, directly below the Schnebly Hill Formation, and the Coconino Sandstone, directly above it, can be seen in many places throughout the greater Four Corners region, but the Schnebly Hill is exposed only within 20 miles of Sedona. The Schnebly Hill rocks are red because a tiny bit of iron in the sediments oxidized during the original erosion, transportation, and deposition of the sediment.

The Schnebly Hill Formation was deposited during a single rise and fall in sea level during Permian time about 275 million years ago. As sea level rose, a finger of ocean called the Pedregosa Sea invaded the area from the southeast, never

reaching much farther than Sedona before retreating back to the southeast. Much of Permian Arizona was a desert environment. Rivers, flowing from mountains in what is now Colorado, carried and deposited silt, sand, and gravel onto floodplains and alluvial fans, now the Hermit Shale. Sedona is built on this soft and easily eroded rock, and it forms the rounded slopes below the colorful cliffs.

The Schnebly Hill Formation was deposited as the invading ocean replaced the floodplains with sandy beaches, silty lagoons, and salty tidal flats. The lower part of the formation, looking like a series of stair steps, is known as the Bell Rock Member. A thorough but brief deepening of the sea laid down a thin hard layer of limestone, the Fort Apache Member, on top of the Bell Rock. Then, as sea level began to fall, beach and lagoon conditions returned, creating the Sycamore Pass

Bell Rock, made of the Bell Rock Member of the Schnebly Hill Formation, stands next to the Red Rock Scenic Byway (AZ 179) between Sedona and Village of Oak Creek.

The spectacular scenery near Sedona is dominated by the red Schnebly Hill Formation, with light-colored Coconino Sandstone capping the higher mesas.

Member. Once the ocean had thoroughly retreated from the region, extensive wind-blown sand dunes covered everything with the Coconino Sandstone. This light-colored formation crowns the higher bluffs north of Sedona. This entire sequence of rocks is especially visible along AZ 179, the Red Rock Scenic Byway, where several roadside pullouts provide outstanding views.

One of Sedona's most famous vistas is of Cathedral Rock soaring above Oak Creek at the Red Rock Crossing Recreation Area.

14. Granite Dells
Weathering along Fractures

The Dells Granite, a 1.4-billion-year-old pluton, is exposed 4 miles north of Prescott along AZ 89. To a geologist, the granite is a bit unusual in that it contains tiny but geochemically significant amounts of uncommon chemical elements, such as rubidium, niobium, yttrium, and uranium. More special, though, is the scenery, for Granite Dells is a spectacular example of spheroidal weathering, a process that results in rounded boulders. At depth below the Earth's surface, a rock of even texture commonly develops a three-dimensional set of fractures, called joints, that break the rock into six-sided blocks. When erosion brings the rock near or to the surface, water is able to penetrate into the joints and begin the weathering processes. First, chemical weathering alters the minerals along the fractures to oxides and clays. Then physical weathering removes the chemical products. The corners and edges of the blocks weather more rapidly than flat faces because they have more surface area to attack, so the rocks become rounded. Eventually, the surface exposures resemble piles of rounded boulders.

Part of the Granite Dells is within Watson Lake Park, a Prescott city park where there are trails and overlooks. Excellent views can also be seen along Granite Dells Road a short distance north of the park.

Watson Lake is surrounded by the Dells Granite.

The pattern of joints that control the spheroidal weathering of the Dells Granite is especially visible along Granite Dells Road.

15. Montezuma Well
A Limestone Sinkhole

Limestone is composed of calcium carbonate (the mineral calcite) and is readily soluble in acid, such as the weak carbonic acid of groundwater. As water percolates through fractured limestone, the rock is slowly dissolved away, leaving behind underground caverns. Should the roof of a cave collapse, a gaping crater, a sinkhole like Montezuma Well, may form.

The Verde Valley was filled with a lake 12 million years ago. Much of the sediment deposited there was limestone, now the Verde Formation, which can be seen along the short hike to the rim of the sinkhole. After the lake drained, underground streams formed caverns in the limestone. One of these collapsed about 11,000 years ago, creating Montezuma Well. The sinkhole is almost 400 feet wide. Its lake stands 70 feet below the rim and is 50 feet deep.

The source of the water in Montezuma Well has yet to be identified. It flows into the sinkhole from underground at a rate of 1,100 gallons per minute. The volume and temperature of that water is constant no matter how the climate may vary from wet to dry. The water flows out of the lake through a small, pipelike cavern more than 300 feet long. Therefore, the lake is not connected to any other surface water, and its biological community has been isolated. Some species, such as shrimp-like amphipods, leeches, and water scorpions, are found only here. Where the outflow emerges, the Sinagua Indians channeled it into an irrigation ditch 1,000 years ago, and it is still in use today. Several small cliff dwellings are within niches inside the sinkhole, and small pueblo structures are scattered about its outside flanks.

The perennial stream that flows from Montezuma Well provides a refreshing oasis within the surrounding desert.

The limestone sinkhole of Montezuma Well is nearly 400 feet wide.

Ruins of several small cliff dwellings lie within the walls of the Montezuma Well sinkhole.

16. Tonto Natural Bridge State Park
Travertine and the Great Unconformity

Natural bridges usually form in sedimentary rock like sandstone, but Tonto Natural Bridge developed within travertine, the fine-grained calcium carbonate deposited during the evaporation of springwater. At 183 feet high above a tunnel 400 feet long and 150 feet wide, it is the largest travertine bridge in the world. The geologic story here began 1.7 billion years ago during the Yavapai-Mazatzal Orogeny, when volcanic eruptions laid down a thick sequence of rhyolite lava flows and ash beds. These form the pinkish orange rocks on the west side of and in the bottom of the canyon. Much, much later, after 1.2 billion years of tumultuous history, sedimentary sandstone and limestone were deposited on top of an eroded surface of the rhyolite in Paleozoic time. This sort of gap in the rock record is called an unconformity, and at places in the canyon near the natural bridge your hand can cover the 1.2-billion-year-gap known as the Great Unconformity. Another unconformity separates the limestone from 2-million-year-old basalt lava flows visible on the mountain where the road first drops into the canyon.

Pine Creek carved its canyon along the weak zone between the Precambrian and Paleozoic rocks. As the Paleozoic limestone was exposed, groundwater seeping through it dissolved calcium carbonate and then redeposited it as layers of travertine on the walls of the canyon. As these layers built out into the canyon, the stream cut into and eventually through the travertine. Tonto Natural Bridge may once have been over 1,000 feet long, but much of it collapsed a few thousand years ago. Most of the fallen travertine debris was dissolved and carried away by Pine Creek.

The view toward the southwest through Tonto Natural Bridge includes a waterfall that drops through a hole in the top of the bridge. The pinkish orange rock in the bottom of the canyon is 1.7-billion-year-old rhyolite.

Modern springs continue to deposit travertine on the canyon walls near Tonto Natural Bridge.

17. Superstition Mountain Caldera
A Volcanic Crater Filled with Ash

The mountain face east of Apache Junction is almost vertical, a sheer rampart that marks the boundary of the Superstition Caldera. At 18.7 million years old, its rhyolite ash flows and beds form the Superstition Mountains. Some researchers think there are six or more calderas here, with smaller craters nested inside of older, larger ones.

When a caldera volcano erupts, great volumes of gas-charged ash are violently blasted out of a magma chamber. When partially empty, the roof of the chamber will collapse, forming a huge circular crater, called a caldera. In the case of the Superstition Caldera, eruptions continued after the collapse. The crater was filled with thousands of feet of ash so hot that the particles fused together into a solid rock called welded tuff. At the same time, renewed pressure within the magma chamber lifted up the central part of the caldera.

The welded tuff within the caldera is resistant to weathering, while the Precambrian metamorphic rocks outside the caldera are fractured and easily eroded. Originally, the top of the ash-filled caldera was probably about even with the surrounding terrain. Now it stands hundreds of feet above the valley because the surrounding rock eroded. Thus, what was once a crater is now a mountain.

The Peralta Trail climbs into the southern margin of the Superstition Caldera. It enters the welded tuff about 0.25 mile from the trailhead and passes through a series of ash flows eroded into fanciful forms. At Fremont Saddle, 2.3 miles from the parking lot, you can see Weavers Needle within the caldera, famous as a landmark in the search for the gold of the Lost Dutchman Mine. The mythical mine in the Superstition Mountains has become legendary, and several people have died looking for it in the rugged terrain.

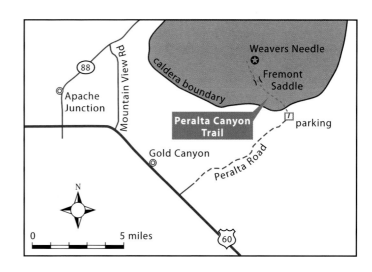

Weavers Needle within the interior of Superstition Mountain Caldera is composed of welded tuff. —U.S. Forest Service, Tonto National Forest

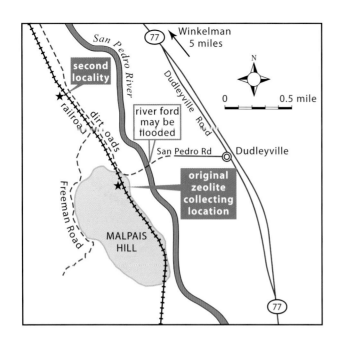

18. Malpais Hill Zeolite Minerals
Curious Crystals in an Unremarkable Hill

Malpais Hill, an unremarkable hill with an appropriate Spanish name, is the eroded remnant of a small basaltic volcano that erupted about 2 million years ago. *Malpais* (pronounced mal-pa-EES) means "badlands" and is often applied to volcanic areas. Basalt commonly contains vugs, the holes left behind by gas bubbles that formed in the still-molten lava. During the last stages in the cooling of the lava, if conditions are right, crystals of zeolite minerals can form within the vugs. Such was the case at Malpais Hill, where the minerals also grew along fracture zones. Mineralogists are interested in the compositional variation of zeolites, and collectors are interested in their beauty.

The most common zeolite mineral at Malpais Hill is heulandite, which forms transparent, bladed crystals as large as 0.25 inch. Much less common and difficult to find are white cubes of chabazite, and tiny bundles of thin erionite needles that sometimes grow into fractures coated with white phillipsite. These other crystals are very small, and magnification is needed to appreciate them. The brown mineral found in some specimens is chalcophanite (zinc-iron-manganese oxide). Black

Glassy crystals of heulandite grow along the edges of vugs coated with pale green celadonite in many Malpais Hill specimens. The field of view is approximately 1.5 inches across.

groutite (manganese oxide-hydroxide) can also be found. Along with milky crystals of calcite, all these minerals often lie on top of pale green celadonite, a type of mica.

The specimen collecting is in a cut along the idle Copper Basin Railway, about 100 yards south of a trestle next to San Pedro Road. You will need a hammer to break open chunks of basalt to reveal the crystal-lined vugs and open the mineralized seams. Additional collecting is available in another railway cut about 1 mile to the north.

Tiny sprays of the rare mineral erionite penetrate some basaltic vugs at Malpais Hill. The field of view in this photo is only 1.6 millimeters across. —Photo by Modris Baum, mindat.org

The mineral collecting at Malpais Hill is along a cut on the idle Copper Basin Railway.

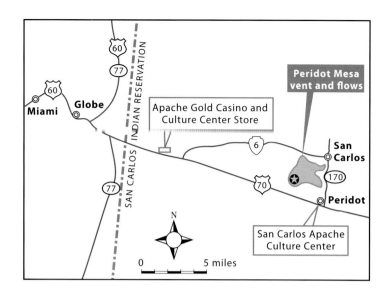

19. Peridot Mesa
Gemstones from the Earth's Interior

Peridot Mesa, the remains of the largest and youngest member of the San Carlos Volcanic Field, is the source of about 90 percent of the world's gem-quality peridot, the birthstone of August. The eruption of Peridot Mesa took place in two nearly simultaneous phases about 500,000 years ago. First an explosive, gas-charged eruption blew out a crater surrounded by a ring of ash and cinders. Then fluid basalt erupted and flowed across the land, forming Peridot Mesa. The basalt contains an extraordinary concentration of iron- and magnesium-rich nodules, most of which are the rock called lherzolite. As large as 20 inches in diameter, the nodules make up as much as 40 percent of the whole rock. Studies of the chemistries and structures of the lherzolite minerals show that the eruption brought the nodules directly to the Earth's

Nodules of lherzolite—essentially, pieces of the Earth's mantle—make up a large portion of the lava at Peridot Mesa (U.S. quarter for scale).

The lherzolite nodules at Peridot Mesa are composed mostly of olivine (light green), along with chrome diopside (emerald green), picotite spinel (amber), and pyroxene (black).

The volcanic cone and lava flows of Peridot Mesa cannot be visited but are visible from US 70.

surface from a depth of at least 20 miles. Thus, the lherzolite provides a window to the mantle, the layer of the Earth below the crust.

Lherzolite is composed largely of the pale yellowish green mineral forsterite, the magnesium-rich variety of olivine. Most of the crystals are the size of sand and gravel, but some approach 2 inches in diameter and yield peridot gemstones. The nodules also contain the minerals chrome diopside (emerald green), pyroxene (lustrous black), and spinel (amber).

Peridot Mesa is within the San Carlos Indian Reservation. Public access is not permitted, but the formation is visible from US 70, and from AZ 170/Indian Route 6 between the communities of Peridot and San Carlos. Rock specimens and peridot jewelry are sold at the San Carlos Apache Culture Center in Peridot.

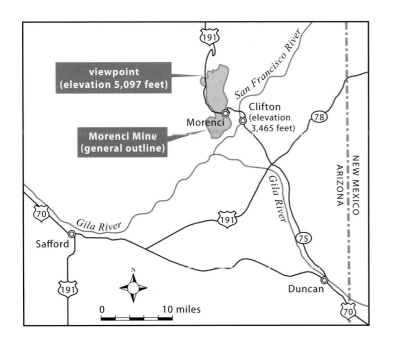

20. Morenci Copper Mine
America's Single Largest Copper Producer

The Morenci Mine is the largest single producer of copper in the United States. (The mine at Bingham Canyon, Utah, is physically larger but produces less metal.) The mineralized area, a copper porphyry in the granitic rock quartz monzonite, was discovered in 1866, and numerous mines were in operation by the middle 1870s. Eventually, there were hundreds of miles of tunnels beneath the towns of Metcalf and Morenci, and smelters operated near the railhead at Clifton. Mining was suspended during the Great Depression but resumed in 1937 with the development of the open pit. Profitable ore lay beneath the original towns, so Metcalf and Morenci were sacrificed; where they were is now a hole in the ground. Today's town of Morenci is a recent development, 3 miles from the original city.

The modern mine, plants, and associated properties cover a total area of 85 square miles. At least 800,000 tons of ore are processed every day. That yielded 614 million pounds of copper in 2011, one-third of Arizona's and fully one-fifth of America's total copper production. You can see the pit from numerous places along steep, winding US 191 (the Coronado Trail Scenic Byway), which follows the edge of the mine for several miles. The viewpoint next to the highway at the upper end of the mine has interpretive signs.

The Morenci Mine from the viewpoint along the Coronado Trail Scenic Byway. —Photo by Phelps Dodge Corporation, courtesy Federal Highway Administration

BASIN AND RANGE PROVINCE
Western Deserts

Westernmost Arizona is within the Basin and Range Province but is quite different from that province in south-central and southeastern Arizona. As part of the geographic Mojave Desert and generally low in elevation, the region is hot and dry. Sparse vegetation and deep erosion mean that the geology, some of the most complex in the Southwest, is well exposed. Extension of the crust was extreme here. For example, in one area the entire Grand Canyon Series of sedimentary rocks was stretched horizontally so that it is only a few tens instead of thousands of feet thick, yet all of the formations are completely recognizable. The area also boasts some of the largest metamorphic core complexes anywhere in the world. Unfortunately, most of that incredible geology is confined to mountains reached only by bad roads and is beyond the scope of this book.

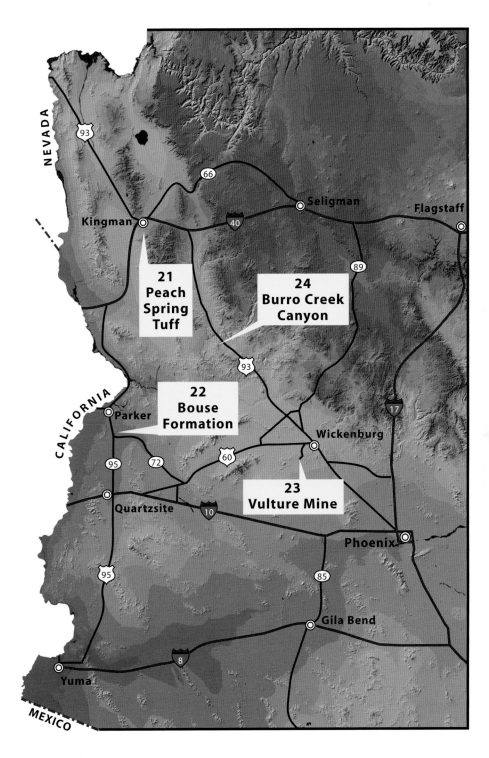

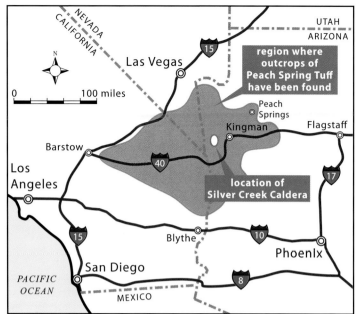

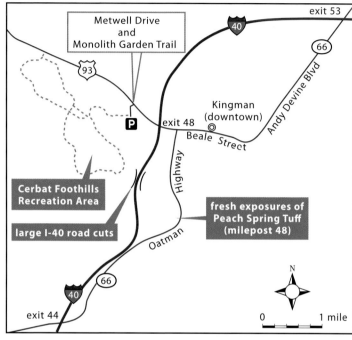

 ## 21. Peach Spring Tuff
Welded Ash from a Mysterious Caldera

The Peach Spring Tuff is a layer of volcanic ash found over an area of nearly 15,000 square miles of the Mojave Desert in western Arizona, eastern California, and southern Nevada. The ash is as much as 420 feet thick near Kingman and thins outward from there; the beds are only 1 to 2 feet thick near Barstow and Blythe, California, and the namesake town of Peach Springs, Arizona. The ash was so hot when it was deposited that its individual ash particles were fused together to form a durable, solid rock, called welded tuff. It probably formed as a series of semimolten flows that raced across the landscape at speeds over 100 miles per hour, and it is possible that the entire formation was laid down in just a few violent days 18.6 million years ago.

Studies indicate that the total original volume of the ash was at least 150 cubic miles. An eruption that large must have created a volcanic caldera 10 to 12 miles across. It was clear that the location of the volcano had to be somewhere near the middle of the ash field, but it was not until 2008 that the location of the Silver Creek Caldera was positively identified on the west side of the Black Mountains, in Arizona between Kingman and the Colorado River. It took so long to identify the volcano because mountain building and erosion since the eruption

Peach Spring Tuff can be collected along the Oatman Highway.

thoroughly altered the landscape and stripped away much of the caldera structure.

The Peach Spring Tuff is well exposed around Kingman. There are excellent exposures in the large road cuts on I-40 just southwest of the city, and the tuff can be sampled at fresh cuts next to road pullouts on the Oatman Highway 1.9 miles south of Beale Street. Hikers can wander among large outcrops along the Monolith Garden Trail in the Cerbat Foothills Recreation Area.

Peach Spring Tuff, a welded volcanic ash, contains numerous crystals of feldspar and broken chips of older rocks (lens cap for scale).

Cliffs of Peach Spring Tuff, here exhibiting columnar jointing, formed as the ash bed cooled, can be seen throughout the Kingman area.

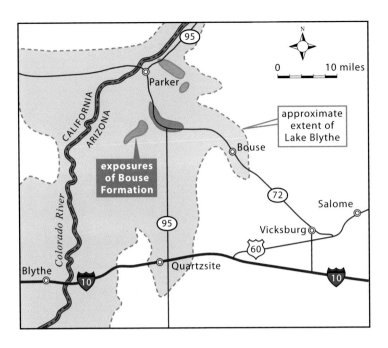

22. Bouse Formation
Deposits from the Carving of the Grand Canyon

As remarkable as it may seem, the mile-deep Grand Canyon has formed only within the last 5.5 million years. A study published in 2011 showed that a long-extinct stream, the Crooked Ridge River that drained from Colorado across northern Arizona, may have started forming the eastern Grand Canyon somewhat earlier, but only a large, through-going Colorado River could have carved the entire Grand Canyon as we see it today. The Bouse Formation, made up of sediment eroded from the Grand Canyon by the Colorado River, is an important piece in solving the puzzle of the carving of the Grand Canyon. The formation, mostly siltstone and sandstone beds a few tens of feet thick, was deposited in two lakes (Lake Mojave in the north and Lake Blythe in the south) that existed in closed desert basins between 5.5 and 5.3 million years ago. Although the formation cannot be age-dated, three related factors constrain its age.

First, north of the Bouse Formation, freshwater limestone was deposited in a different, slightly older lake along Arizona's Grand Wash. Volcanic ash at the top of that limestone is 6 million years old. Had the muddy Colorado River existed at that time, then sand and gravel, not limestone, would have been deposited in Grand Wash. Second, another layer of volcanic ash is found underneath the Lake Mojave part of the Bouse Formation. Its age of 5.5 million years indicates that the river still did not exist at that time. Third, by 5.3 million years ago the Colorado River began depositing fossil-bearing sand and gravel near Yuma, Arizona, and California's Imperial Valley. Therefore, the modern Colorado River apparently formed and began carving the Grand Canyon between 5.5 and 5.3 million years ago. Although it is exposed in many places, one of the best areas to see the rounded, cobble-covered hills of the Bouse Formation is along AZ 95 near its junction with AZ 72 south of Parker.

Low hills composed of the Bouse Formation lie along AZ 95 and AZ 72 south of Parker.

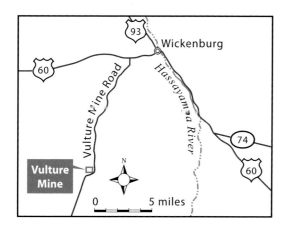

23. Vulture Mountains and Mine
Gold and Silver amid Complex Geology

In 1863, Henry Wickenburg found an outcrop of altered granitic rock shot through by quartz veins loaded with gold. He named the deposit the Vulture because vultures soared overhead as he made the discovery. During its lifetime, the Vulture Mine produced at least 340,000 ounces of gold and 240,000 ounces of silver, making it Arizona's largest and richest noncopper, precious metal mine before the operation ended in 1942.

The geology of the Vulture Mountains is quite complex. The core of the range is composed of Precambrian igneous and metamorphic rocks. During the Laramide Orogeny about 70 million years ago, the old rocks were intruded by quartz monzonite, an igneous rock similar to granite but with less quartz and more plagioclase feldspar. The Vulture gold deposit formed along and within a dike of the monzonite. Extensive volcanic activity during the Miocene Epoch, about 20 million years ago, covered the area with rhyolite and basalt lavas, and some air-fall tuffs. Not long after that, large-scale extension stretched the area, moving huge blocks of the rocks horizontally while also rotating them vertically. Some lava flows,

The old Precambrian granite of the Vulture Mountains tends to be severely altered and faulted, as can be seen in road cuts along Vulture Mine Road.

originally flat-lying, are now standing on end. Finally, normal faulting during development of the Basin and Range Province sliced the area into blocks, including today's Vulture Mountains.

Access to the mountains and the mine is on Vulture Mine Road, south from US 60 in the western part of Wickenburg. The 12 miles of this public road pass through examples of all the geology: first the Cretaceous monzonite, then brushing by volcanic hills and crossing several of the faults before traversing the Precambrian granite and schist near the mine. The Vulture Mine is private property that charges an entry fee, although the property is often closed. In addition to the mine, there are extensive remains of the mill and the town of Vulture City, which supposedly once had a population of 5,000.

A bed of light-colored rhyolite ash that was tilted and then faulted is clearly exposed along Vulture Mine Road.

Outcrops of quartz monzonite in the Vulture Mountains are light colored, tend to be rounded, and often are covered with yellowish green lichen.

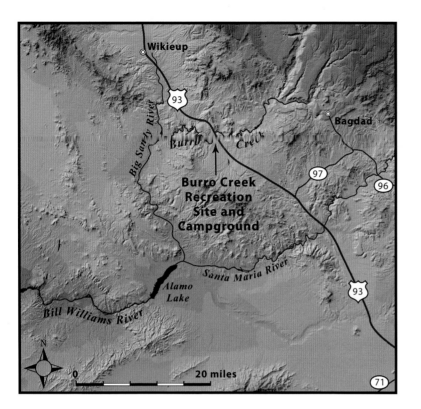

 ## 24. Burro Creek Canyon
Sheer Cliffs in Lava Flows

Along US 93 between Wikieup and the Santa Maria River is a rugged area where the Hualapai Mountains to the west and Aquarius Mountains to the east, both largely composed of Precambrian granite and gneiss, converge at a thick sequence of Tertiary lava flows known as the Kaiser Spring Volcanic Field. These volcanoes were active between 22 and 8 million years ago. The highway traverses the edge of the volcanic plateau into which the rivers have carved deep canyons. The most spectacular and accessible of these is Burro Creek Canyon, which is nearly 300 feet deep below the highway bridge and grows deeper upstream to the east.

The Kaiser Spring volcanoes erupted lavas that varied in composition from basalt to andesite to rhyolite, depending on how much silica it contained. Some andesite has small but abundant shiny black crystals of pyroxene. Some basalt flows bear occasional glassy green crystals of olivine and often have small gas bubble holes. Near the campground are a few light-colored beds of rhyolite ash.

The canyon is visible from the US 93 bridge, but you can also hike up the canyon from the Burro Creek Campground, enjoy a perennial stream in the midst of the desert, and see the rocks up close.

Burro Creek Canyon upstream from the US 93 bridge. Note the light-colored ash beds in the lower right and the dark basalt forming the upper cliffs.

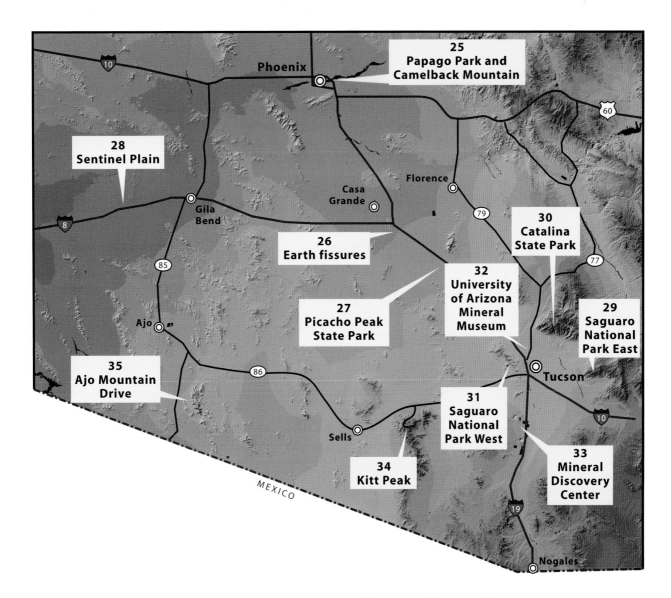

25
Papago Park and
Camelback Mountain

Phoenix

28
Sentinel Plain

Florence

30
Catalina
State Park

Casa
Grande

26
Earth fissures

32
University
of Arizona
Mineral
Museum

29
Saguaro
National
Park East

Gila
Bend

27
Picacho Peak
State Park

35
Ajo Mountain
Drive

Ajo

Tucson

31
Saguaro
National
Park West

33
Mineral
Discovery
Center

Sells

34
Kitt Peak

MEXICO

Nogales

BASIN AND RANGE PROVINCE
South-central Arizona

South-central Arizona, part of the Basin and Range Province, includes the most densely populated part of the state. Important geologic sites are within the Phoenix and Tucson city limits, and many more are in the surrounding region. This area features some of the best known and easily visited examples of metamorphic core complexes and detachment faulting (uplifted in some cases by later normal faulting), numerous important mines, environmental hazards because of groundwater pumping, a national observatory, and several national and state parks.

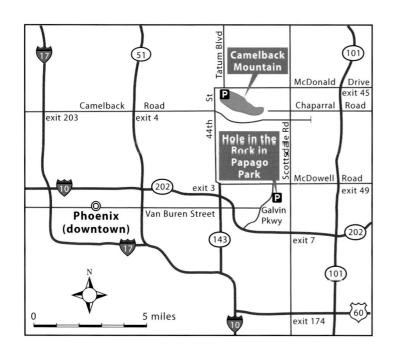

25. Papago Park and Camelback Mountain
Ancient Landslides and the Great Unconformity

The small hill of Hole in the Rock, the Papago Buttes, and Camelback Mountain, which is indeed shaped much like a kneeling camel, stand above the flat valley floor around Phoenix and Scottsdale. They tell a very special and complex geologic story. The rock exposed at the base of Hole in the Rock and which forms the eastern part (the "body") of Camelback Mountain is Camelback Granite, formed during the Yavapai-Mazatzal Orogeny about 1.8 billion years ago. The granite is coarse grained with large crystals of orthoclase feldspar plus abundant biotite mica that has been altered to a greenish color.

The outcrops of Hole in the Rock and the other Papago Buttes, and the rock that forms the western part (the "head") of Camelback Mountain is Camels Head Formation, about 25 million years old. The Camels Head is a very coarse sedimentary breccia, a rock composed of angular fragments held together with a matrix of sand and silt. The Camels Head includes chunks of granite and other old rocks that are inches to several feet in dimension. Huge blocks of granite—hundreds of feet long—were once mapped as part of the bedrock rather

The "head" of Camelback Mountain (at left) is composed of Camels Head Formation of Tertiary age while the "body" of the camel is Camelback Granite of Precambrian age. The contact between the two formations at the camel's "neck" is the Great Unconformity. —Photo by Dru Bloomfield, Creative Commons

than as fragments within the breccia! The only way such massive materials could have been deposited in a sedimentary environment would be via landslides, rock avalanches, or debris flows at the base of a steep mountain.

Uplift during the Laramide Orogeny followed by erosion exposed the Camelback Granite, and extension and faulting formed steep mountains. In a huge landslide or debris flow, the far younger Camels Head Formation was deposited on top of the old granite. The contact between the two rock units is a huge gap in time called the Great Unconformity. You can easily spread your hand across this span of more than 1.7 billion years. Basin and Range faults uplifted the rocks into a series of low ridges, some of which, including the Papago Buttes and Camelback Mountain, remain exposed above young valley-fill alluvium.

Parking and a short hike are easier at Hole in the Rock in Papago Park, just off Galvin Parkway between the Arizona Botanical Gardens and the Phoenix Zoo. At Camelback Mountain, parking in a small lot next to McDonald Drive is at a premium, and the trail to the unconformity at the "neck" of the mountain is longer and steeper.

The Great Unconformity at the base of Hole in the Rock in Phoenix's Papago Park. The unconformity surface runs from lower left to upper right through the middle of this photo, with Precambrian Camelback Granite below and Tertiary Camels Head Formation above.

Hole in the Rock is one of the Papago Buttes.

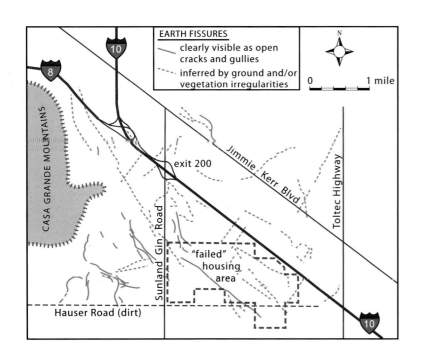

EARTH FISSURES
— clearly visible as open cracks and gullies
--- inferred by ground and/or vegetation irregularities

0   1 mile

CASA GRANDE MOUNTAINS

exit 200

Sunland Gin Road

Jimmie Kerr Blvd

Toltec Highway

"failed" housing area

Hauser Road (dirt)

26. Earth Fissures
Deep Cracks from Groundwater Pumping

Deep underground in valley basins filled with unconsolidated sediment, water occupies pore spaces between particles. If groundwater is pumped out faster than natural recharge can replace it, then rock particles lose support and settle closer together. As the sediment is compressed, the ground above settles, a process called subsidence, and cracks, or fissures, open along the ground surface. Near the mountains at the edges of the valleys, solid bedrock is close to the surface and there is little or no subsidence. Earth fissures develop between there and the deeper sedimentary fill of the valley. The open cracks are up to 10 feet wide and hundreds of feet long. Many are later enlarged by stream runoff and become hosts for vegetation more lush and dense than on the surrounding ground. Earth fissures and land subsidence force the redesign of agricultural

A newly developed fissure near the Picacho Mountains. Note the cracks and small hole in the foreground, where the soil is beginning to collapse. —Arizona Geological Survey

56

irrigation systems; necessitate the repair of water wells, sewer pipes, natural gas lines, and roads; and destroy buildings.

Earth fissures have been found in many places in Arizona's Maricopa, Pinal, Pima, and Cochise counties. Notable is the Santa Cruz Basin in Pinal County between Phoenix and Tucson, where farmers began pumping groundwater around 1900. Several hundred million acre feet of water have been pumped out (1 acre foot is 325,851 gallons). The water table has dropped more than 500 feet in some areas, resulting in ground subsidence as great as 30 feet.

Three readily accessible sets of earth fissures are conveniently located near I-10. One set is just south of exit 200 along Sunland Gin and Hauser roads. Between the freeway and the Casa Grande Mountains, dozens of fissures cross the landscape, enter into an aborted housing project, and impinge on the roads. East of the freeway at exit 190, another fissure more than 2 miles long parallels the west face of the Signal Peak Hills just north of Woodruff Road and east of Camino Rica Drive. A third zone crosses I-10 near milepost 216 just north of Picacho Peak (see Site 27 map).

A newly developed fissure near Kansas Settlement in Cochise County. Note the plant roots that extend across the opening, which exposes lakebeds deposited in Lake Cochise during Pleistocene time. —Arizona Geological Survey

Earth fissures often develop into stream channels and unofficial dumps.

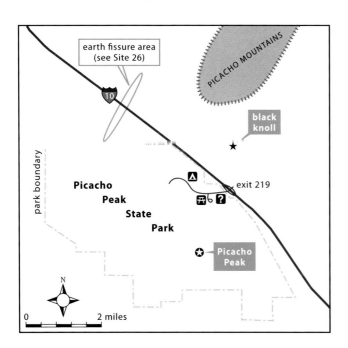

27. Picacho Peak State Park
Volcanic but Not a Volcano

Picacho Peak stands alone as a prominent landmark adjacent to I-10 between Phoenix and Tucson. Composed mostly of basalt, it looks like a volcanic neck, the eroded pipelike core of a volcano, and that is how it was long identified. Unlike a neck, which tends to be massive and with a vertical structure, the peak is composed of numerous lava flows, 22 million years old and now altered, faulted, and tilted toward the northeast. Near the summit is a block of much older granite. Old intrusive igneous rock like that certainly should not be on top of younger lava flows.

Geologists now realize that Picacho Peak represents the upper plate of a metamorphic core complex. The Picacho Mountains a few miles to the northeast are the lower plate. Extension of the Earth's crust led to the formation of a detachment fault, a nearly horizontal fault that allowed the rocks of Picacho Peak and the little black knoll east of the freeway to literally slide across the underlying rocks of the mountains. (This process is more fully described in the introduction.)

That granite near top of the peak? It probably represents a chunk of the Picacho Mountain core, possibly 1.4-billion-year-old Oracle Granite, that broke off during the volcanic eruptions. After it was carried along within a lava flow, erosion just happens to have left it exposed near the top of the mountain.

Picacho Peak is a prominent landmark next to I-10 between Tucson and Phoenix.

The small black knoll in the middle of the valley is a fragment of the upper plate of the Picacho Detachment Fault that includes Picacho Peak. The distant Picacho Mountains are the metamorphic core complex of the lower plate.

28. Sentinel Plain Volcanic Field
Far-flowing Flood Basalts

The Sentinel Plain volcanoes are quite different from most of the volcanoes elsewhere in Arizona. The eruptions were voluminous yet quiet and formed no obvious tall volcanic cones. The field formed between 1.9 and 1.2 million years ago and covered 225 square miles with lava flows that total as much as 130 feet thick.

About twenty centers erupted lava onto the Sentinel Plain. Some were long fissures that repeatedly poured highly fluid lava onto the surface, where it flowed evenly in all directions as flood basalt. Other, more localized centers developed shield volcanoes, mountains much wider than they are high. Basalt is more fluid than other lava, so it can flow long distances before cooling, building wide volcanoes. Sentinel Peak is the largest of these. It is nearly 20,000 feet across at its base yet only 250 feet high—almost eighty times wider than it is tall. The Sentinel Plain's other shields are considerably smaller.

The Sentinel Plain Volcanic Field along Agua Caliente Road with Sentinel Peak in the distance.

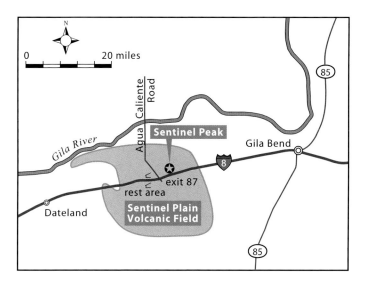

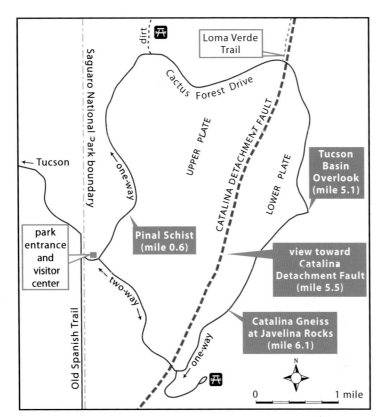

29. Saguaro National Park, East
Catalina Detachment Fault

Rarely can you see the lower plate, the upper plate, and the detachment fault of a metamorphic core complex all in one place. That's part of the reason they are so difficult to envision. But you can see all three parts in the east unit of Saguaro National Park. This example is so good, in fact, that the Geological Society of America included it in a volume about the best geologic sites in the western United States. Here, a huge amount of intact rock of the upper plate slid west along the Catalina Detachment Fault.

Cactus Forest Drive is a one-way loop road that begins at the park's visitor center. The first few miles cross rocks of the upper plate. About 0.6 mile from the drive's entrance is a small canyon where metamorphic rock called Pinal Schist is nicely exposed. Although this is some of the oldest rock in Arizona, dating to around 1.7 billion years ago, it lies above the detachment fault that exposed the igneous intrusions of the lower plate.

The road passes from the upper plate onto the lower plate when it crosses the Catalina Detachment Fault (buried and not visible at this point) at the Loma Verde Trail. During the climb toward the Tucson Basin Overlook, look east at the Rincon Mountains. They are the lower plate, rock that once

The Catalina Gneiss is strongly foliated and banded (lens cap for scale).

The Pinal Schist is part of the upper plate of the Catalina Detachment Fault.

The Catalina Detachment Fault is visible where it separates light gray limestones in the upper plate (right) from darker metamorphic rocks in the lower plate (left).

The Javelina Rocks are composed of Catalina Gneiss in the lower plate of the Catalina Detachment Fault.

was far below the surface and covered by thousands of feet of upper plate rock. Now look to the west. Most of that upper plate material now lies buried under young sand and gravel beneath Tucson, with one large block forming the Tucson Mountains west of the city (Site 31).

About 5.5 miles from the visitor center, you can look down to the west and see the path of the Catalina Detachment Fault crossing low ridges, where it separates light-colored limestones of late Paleozoic age in the upper plate from darker, brownish rocks in the lower plate.

Javelina Rocks, at mile 6.1, are an outstanding example of the lower plate's Catalina Gneiss, a rock whose origin puzzles geologists. Before being metamorphosed during the extreme stretching that produced the Basin and Range Province, this rock might have been Oracle Granite. Others feel Precambrian sediments called the Apache Group are more likely. Both rock units are about 1.4 billion years old and are exposed in the Santa Catalina Mountains to the northwest. In either case, metamorphism at an estimated depth of 7 miles stretched, sheared, and recrystallized the rock into this distinctive banded gneiss, the core of the metamorphic core complex.

Returning back toward the visitor center, the road again crosses the detachment fault just west of the turn off to Javelina Picnic Area. Although the fault is not visible, the shallow valley north of the road marks its trace.

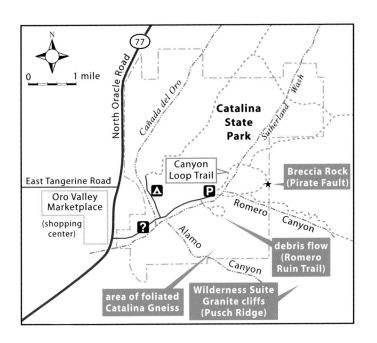

30. Catalina State Park
Steep Mountain Face along the Pirate Fault

The Santa Catalina Mountains are part of the same large metamorphic core complex discussed in Site 29. We have the Pirate Fault to thank for exposing it here, along with its wide variety of rock types. During the formation of the Basin and Range Province between 25 and 5 million years ago, the mountains rose along the Pirate Fault, a high-angle normal fault. Rocks have moved up along the fault as much as 10,000 feet with respect to Oro Valley to the west. The most recent movement happened about 6 million years ago, but the mountain face is geologically fresh and reveals the metamorphic core rock formations. All of the rocks on the mountain face are in the lower plate of the Catalina Detachment Fault. The fault and its upper plate were dropped down by the Pirate Fault and are now hidden beneath the young sedimentary fill of the valley.

Map labels:
- North Oracle Road
- 77
- Cañada del Oro
- Sutherland Wash
- **Catalina State Park**
- Canyon Loop Trail
- Breccia Rock (Pirate Fault)
- Romero Canyon
- East Tangerine Road
- Oro Valley Marketplace (shopping center)
- Alamo Canyon
- Romero Canyon
- debris flow (Romero Ruin Trail)
- area of foliated Catalina Gneiss
- Wilderness Suite Granite cliffs (Pusch Ridge)
- 0   1 mile

View to the south of the straight west face of the Santa Catalina Mountains, controlled by the Pirate Fault.

Breccia Rock, gneiss shattered by movements along the Pirate Fault, is in the fault zone.

The northeast-southwest-trending Pirate Fault runs along the base of the straight mountain face. The channels of the Cañada del Oro and Sutherland washes, which parallel the fault, have eroded in the crushed rock of the fault zone. An easy hike of 0.8 mile along the Canyon Loop Trail leads to one of the few places where the Pirate fault zone is actually exposed. Breccia Rock, the prominent, light tan outcrop at the base of the mountains, is composed of gneiss shattered by the fault movement.

The most prominent rock formation on the mountain face is the 50-million-year-old Wilderness Suite Granite. It forms the vertical pinnacles and cliffs of Pusch Ridge high above Alamo Canyon. Near the base of the mountains is Catalina Gneiss, which is part of the mountain's core. Large-scale metamorphic banding is visible near Alamo Canyon, especially in low

afternoon sunlight. The smoother mountainsides farther north are composed of 28-million-year-old Catalina Granite.

The steep, young mountains have also generated debris flows. Visible along the Canyon Loop, Romero Ruin, and other park trails are wide areas covered with jumbled rocks, some of which are several feet in diameter and weigh as much as 1,000 tons. The boulders, chunks of Wilderness Suite Granite and Catalina Gneiss, were rafted into place by slurries of mud and rock with a water content as low as 20 percent. Debris flows are known to travel out of mountain canyons with tremendous momentum, moving faster than 20 miles per hour with a consistency much like wet concrete. Although these flows formed in the past 10,000 to 20,000 years, they likely occurred during flash floods associated with heavy summertime thunderstorms, conditions that can occur today.

The curving pattern visible on the lower slopes of the Santa Catalina Mountains is the metamorphic banding of the Catalina Gneiss, while the crest of the range is composed of Wilderness Suite Granite.

Boulder-covered area of a debris flow along the Canyon Loop Trail. The large saguaros are about 30 feet tall.

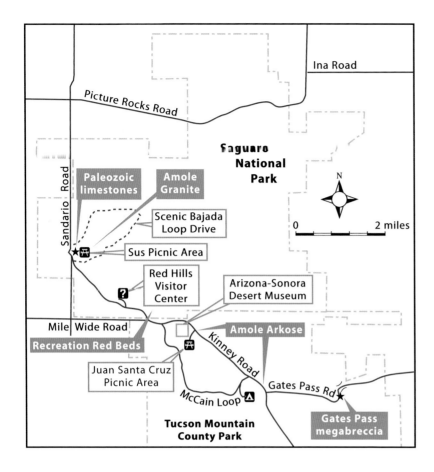

31. Saguaro National Park, West
The Tucson Mountains

Imagine a setting where, over millions of years, sedimentary rocks were occasionally laid down between long intervals of erosion. Then magma intruded the region. A huge volcano formed and covered the landscape with lava flows and ashfalls before collapsing into a gigantic, 12-by-15-mile-wide caldera. Long after that, this entire assemblage was transported by detachment faulting to a place many miles from where it formed. Finally, it was uplifted, tilted, and eroded as part of the Basin and Range Province. This is the Tucson Mountains, a geologic treasure immediately west of downtown Tucson that also is home to the west unit of Saguaro National Park, Tucson

Mountain County Park, the world-famous Arizona-Sonora Desert Museum, and the Old Tucson movie studios.

To see the mountain's geology in mostly chronological order, you should start in the north at the Sus Picnic Area. The rock there and in the ridge to the east is Amole Granite, which fits at the very end of this story, but the hill west of the picnic area includes gray limestone formations of Paleozoic age, deposited when the entire region was beneath a shallow sea. Extensively exposed elsewhere in southeast Arizona, only a few small remnants are scattered around the edges of the Tucson Mountains.

Saguaro National Park's Red Hills Visitor Center was named for the Recreation Red Beds, stream-laid sandstone and conglomerate deposited during Jurassic time. The red beds are exposed along Kinney Road between the visitor center and the Arizona-Sonora Desert Museum. Studies of the tree rings in petrified conifer logs found in the red beds suggest the trees grew in a seasonal subtropical climate.

Farther east are exposures of Amole Arkose, a "dirty" sandstone containing angular sand-sized grains of feldspar minerals and chips of older rocks. Sandstones are considered dirty if they are not made almost entirely of rounded quartz grains. The arkose was deposited in and near an extensive lake during Cretaceous time. This age is based largely on the bones of a single hadrosaur dinosaur found in the arkose. The formation is visible everyplace along Kinney Road between the Arizona-Sonora Desert Museum and Gates Pass Road but is especially well exposed in a road cut at the entrance to the Juan Santa Cruz Picnic Area.

As Gates Pass Road climbs toward Gates Pass, it enters the Cat Mountain Tuff, the volcanic rock exploded from the Tucson Mountain Caldera about 70 million years ago. Much of the formation is a megabreccia named the Tucson Mountain Chaos. It contains huge blocks of older rocks, such as Recreation Red Beds and Amole Arkose, that were broken, tumbled, and incorporated within the tuff

Small outcrops of gray Paleozoic limestone formations are visible on the hill west of the Sus Picnic Area.

Iron oxide imparts the red color to the Recreation Red Beds.

You can see bedding layers in the Amole Arkose in the road cut at the entrance to the Juan Santa Cruz Picnic Area.

Most of the higher parts of the Tucson Mountains are capped by the Cat Mountain Tuff, the volcanic ash erupted by the Tucson Mountain Caldera.

during the explosion and collapse that formed the caldera. Some blocks measure tens to even hundreds of feet across. One of these is exposed in the road cut just southwest of the parking lot at the top of Gates Pass.

Now recall the Amole Granite exposed at the Sus Picnic Area. It solidified from magma remaining belowground at the end of the caldera's eruption. No doubt the granite lies at depth beneath most of the Tucson Mountains.

The entire Tucson Mountains block moved about 16 miles from the northeast along the Catalina Detachment Fault. The root of the magma system that fed the Tucson Mountain Caldera must lie someplace near the Catalina Mountains. Some geologists think it is below the intersection of Oracle and Ina roads, hidden beneath the alluvial fill of the valley.

The Amole Granite is very coarse grained and composed mostly of pinkish orthoclase feldspar plus glassy quartz (lens cap for scale).

The Amole Granite at the Sus Picnic Area weathers to sand.

A specimen of azurite, malachite, and chrysocolla from the Morenci Mine on display in the University of Arizona Mineral Museum.

32. University of Arizona Mineral Museum
A World-class Collection

The University of Arizona Mineral Museum, begun as part of the Arizona Territorial Museum in 1892, became a separate facility in 1919. With more than twenty-seven thousand mineral specimens (about two thousand on display at any one time), it is one of the largest and most comprehensive mineral collections in the United States. The scope is worldwide but emphasizes minerals from Arizona and Mexico. There also is an extensive collection of meteorites. Special exhibitions display minerals from world-class localities such as Bisbee, Arizona, and Mapimi, Mexico; individual mineral species such as turquoise; or donated collections of note.

The museum is located within the Flandrau Science Center on the campus of the University of Arizona, near downtown Tucson. It is a nonprofit organization supported by the university, regional mining companies, the Tucson Gem and Mineral Society, and public donations.

Rotating displays of minerals from famous localities, such as this one showing Bisbee specimens, are a feature of the University of Arizona Mineral Museum.

A specimen of calcite from Bisbee in the University of Arizona Mineral Museum. The red color is from chalcotrichite, a fine-grained copper oxide contained within the calcite crystals.

33. Mineral Discovery Center and Mission Mine
Open Pit Copper Mine on Tour

The Mission Mine is the only open pit mine in Arizona that offers a visitor center, museum, and regular guided tours. It is one of several open pit operations in the Sierrita Mountains, where mines have been worked since the 1880s. The modern mine was started in 1961 after exploratory drilling revealed a porphyry copper deposit. In a porphyry, copper is disseminated throughout the rock, not concentrated in veins. To obtain the ore, miners must remove all the rock, crush it, and then process it to extract the copper. The pit measures about 2 by 1.75 miles wide and 1,400 feet deep. The total amount of earth moved as of 2010 is said to be six times greater than that moved in digging the Panama Canal! The ore averages only about 0.5 percent copper by weight, yet the mine yields 100,000 tons (200 million pounds) of copper plus 2 million ounces of silver per year.

This haul truck is capable of carrying 120 tons of ore. Trucks now in use are much larger than this.

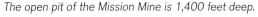

The open pit of the Mission Mine is 1,400 feet deep.

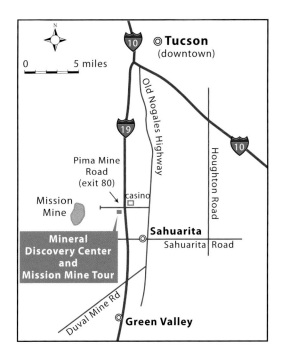

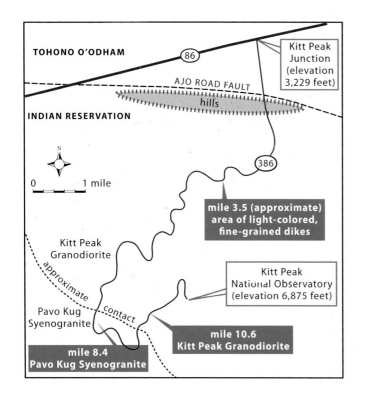

TOHONO O'ODHAM

86

AJO ROAD FAULT

hills

INDIAN RESERVATION

N

0   1 mile

Kitt Peak
Junction
(elevation
3,229 feet)

386

**mile 3.5 (approximate)
area of light-colored,
fine-grained dikes**

Kitt Peak
Granodiorite

approximate

contact

Pavo Kug
Syenogranite

Kitt Peak
National Observatory
(elevation 6,875 feet)

**mile 10.6
Kitt Peak Granodiorite**

**mile 8.4
Pavo Kug Syenogranite**

34. Kitt Peak
A Suite of Unusual Granitic Rocks

More than twenty telescopes scan the sky from Kitt Peak National Observatory, located at this high-elevation site in the Tohono O'odham Indian Reservation because of atmospheric stability, distance from city lights, and accessibility. Kitt Peak is composed mostly of two intrusive igneous rocks, the Kitt Peak Granodiorite and the Pavo Kug Syenogranite, that formed during Jurassic time, about 165 million years ago. AZ 386 steeply winds its way 12.2 miles up to the summit of Kitt Peak, which is south of and 3,650 feet higher than AZ 86. There are many pullouts, and road cuts provide excellent exposures of the rocks. Drivers should note the mileage at the turnoff from AZ 86.

AZ 386 first crosses through some low hills composed of Pan Tak Granite, a 58-million-year-old rock unrelated to those of Kitt Peak. The hills, best seen as the highway begins the climb onto the mountain, are probably an old, eroded scarp along the Ajo Road Fault. Then, about 3.5 miles from the turnoff are light-colored, fine-grained dikes of Pan Tak Granite that intruded along fractures in the Kitt Peak Granodiorite. Some dikes contain reddish grains of garnet, but unfortunately there are no road pullouts close to the best examples of these dikes.

The Pavo Kug Syenogranite has large masses of greasy quartz (U.S. quarter for scale).

High on the mountain, the highway crosses from Kitt Peak Granodiorite into Pavo Kug Syenogranite. A pullout at mile 8.4 is a good place to examine the latter, a silica-rich rock characterized by big greasy-looking masses of quartz accompanied by white orthoclase feldspar and little else. As the road curves back toward the north, it crosses back into Kitt Peak Granodiorite. A pullout at 10.6 miles is a good place to examine it. The granodiorite contains large crystals of orthoclase feldspar up to 1.5 inches long, occasional small honey-colored crystals of sphene, and black crystals of hornblende amphibole and biotite mica. Occasional veinlets, with black tourmaline and green epidote, cut the rock.

The large Mayall Telescope towers above outcrops of Kitt Peak Granodiorite.

The Kitt Peak Granodiorite is speckled with small, dark crystals of hornblende and biotite (lens cap for scale).

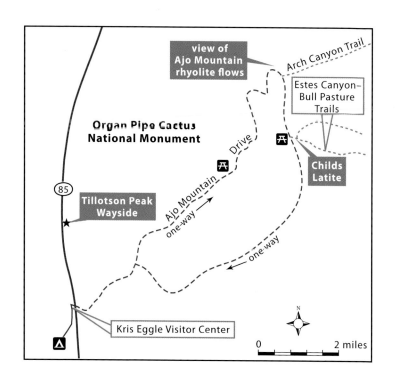

view of
Ajo Mountain
rhyolite flows

Arch Canyon Trail

Estes Canyon–
Bull Pasture
Trails

Organ Pipe Cactus
National Monument

Ajo Mountain Drive

85

Tillotson Peak
Wayside

Childs
Latite

Ajo Mountain
one-way

one-way

Kris Eggle Visitor Center

N

0   2 miles

35. Organ Pipe Cactus National Monument
Strange Volcanic Rock in the Ajo Mountains

The Ajo Mountains in Organ Pipe Cactus National Monument are part of an extensive volcanic field of rhyolite ash flow tuffs and lava flows with a total thickness of about 2,000 feet. Unlike Arizona's other rhyolite fields, there is no gigantic caldera here; these rocks were erupted from numerous volcanic vents roughly 18 million years ago. The best way to experience these rocks is along Ajo Mountain Drive, a 21-mile loop road that mostly is rough but improved dirt. Forming sheer cliffs along the mountain front, the rhyolite is especially spectacular at Arch Canyon, where natural arches have eroded into the tuff.

A special member of this volcanic suite is the Childs Latite, a volcanic rock of intermediate composition, containing more silica than basalt and andesite but less than rhyolite. In most cases, the minerals that compose a volcanic rock cooled quickly from lava are nearly microscopic in size. The Childs Latite contains a large proportion of well-formed plagioclase feldspar crystals as much as 1 inch long. These crystals must

The Childs Latite has a great abundance of large feldspar crystals (lens cap for scale).

74

have formed when the magma was slowly cooling in a chamber below the Earth's surface. When erupted onto the surface, partially crystallized magma like this will usually flow only a short distance, forming short, thick lava flows. However, Childs Latite occurs as thin flows over an area greater than 2,000 square miles. It seems likely that the magma contained an unusually high percentage of gases such as water and carbon dioxide that made it more fluid than usual. You can see this spectacular rock at the parking area for and near the start of the Estes Canyon–Bull Pasture Trails. It can also be found on a short walk into the hills just southeast of the Tillotson Peak Wayside, on AZ 85.

Fragments of older rocks were enclosed within ashfalls on the slopes of erupting volcanoes, forming a rock called tuff breccia.

Columnar jointing is well developed in some rhyolite lava flows of the Ajo Mountains.

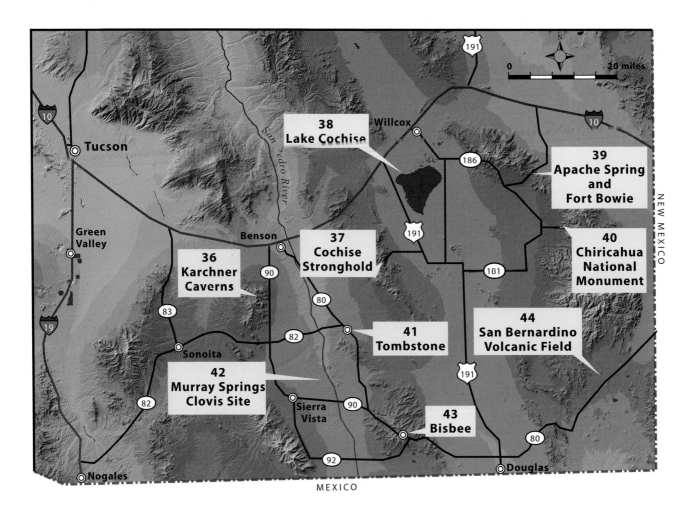

38 Lake Cochise

39 Apache Spring and Fort Bowie

40 Chiricahua National Monument

37 Cochise Stronghold

36 Karchner Caverns

44 San Bernardino Volcanic Field

41 Tombstone

42 Murray Springs Clovis Site

43 Bisbee

Tucson

Green Valley

Willcox

Benson

Sonoita

Sierra Vista

Nogales

Douglas

NEW MEXICO

MEXICO

BASIN AND RANGE PROVINCE
Southeast Arizona

Southeast Arizona, the state's best expression of the Basin and Range Province, contains rocks of all ages. The oldest are Precambrian gneiss and schist that initially formed during the Yavapai-Mazatzal Orogeny more than 1.7 billion years ago. Thick sequences of sedimentary rocks were laid down during the Paleozoic and Mesozoic eras. The Laramide Orogeny formed numerous plutons of granitic rocks and some of Arizona's richest mineral deposits. During the orogeny the older rocks were compressed and moved by large-scale thrust faults. Later, basin-and-range normal faults broke the rocks into the modern valleys and mountains. All this is capped by volcanic rocks from Tertiary and Quaternary time. The mountain building continues, too. Although Arizona is not considered to be earthquake country, occasional tremors do take place. The largest historic earthquake was the Pitaycachi shock that took place on May 4, 1887. Centered a few miles south of the Mexican border below the San Bernardino Valley, the magnitude 7.2 quake destroyed buildings in Bisbee and Tombstone and caused significant damage as far away as Tucson.

36. Kartchner Caverns State Park
An Extraordinary Limestone Cave

In 1974, two spelunkers were exploring the base of the Whetstone Mountains, looking for a new cave to explore. What they found was an extraordinary place, a limestone cavern still wet and growing. Kartchner Caverns is within a fault block composed of Escabrosa Formation, a pure limestone deposited in Carboniferous time. Numerous faults, which cut the block, control the northeast-to-southwest arrangement of underground passageways. A long process led to state park approval, and years of careful development were needed before Kartchner Caverns opened for tours in 1999. Because the cave had not been visited by thousands of people before its protection, its fragile formations are intact and well preserved.

Aside from the usual stalactites, stalagmites, and flowstone typical of limestone caves, Kartchner Caverns includes unique decorations. The world's most extensive brushite moonmilk, a calcium phosphate mineral formed by a chemical reaction between bat guano and limestone, is here. Nitrocalcite, a rare nitrate mineral, forms and disappears depending on the humidity of air blowing through the cave entrance. Coral pipes look very much like coral stems on a tropical reef. Turnip shields that look like vegetables hanging from the ceiling have been found nowhere else; they form along vertical cracks in the cave roof, but exactly how is unclear. Growths of needlelike quartz crystals that look like bird nests are another mystery but may have formed within the fault zones before the cave existed. The cave also features the longest soda-straw stalactite in the world—21 feet 3 inches long. Whatever the form, many decorations are colored various shades of red and yellow by iron oxide minerals brought in by mineralizing solutions from igneous and metamorphic rocks that surround the cavern's limestone block.

The Rotunda/Throne Room Tour is available all year (reservations recommended), while the Big Room Tour is closed from mid-April to mid-October in deference to nesting bats.

Formations inside Kartchner Caverns. –
Photo by Noelle Wilson, © Arizona State Parks

37. Cochise Stronghold
A Warrior's Hideaway among Granitic Domes

The Dragoon Mountains feature complex geology mostly hidden away from maintained roads, but Cochise Stronghold is readily accessible. During the Laramide Orogeny a thick sequence of Paleozoic and Mesozoic sedimentary rocks atop a core of Precambrian schist were deformed before being sliced by a series of west-to-east thrust faults. As the orogeny came to its end, a number of igneous plutons were intruded along the faults. The youngest of these, dating to about 23 million years ago, is the Stronghold Granite, a single intrusion of relatively small size. Still later, as a part of the Basin and Range Province, the Dragoon Mountains were uplifted and eroded, exposing the granite and surrounding rock. Although officially named Stronghold Granite, the rock is actually granodiorite. This type of igneous rock has less quartz than true granite, about equal abundance of the two feldspars (orthoclase and plagioclase), and both black biotite and white muscovite.

Although the granodiorite is a massive, solid rock that forms huge domes, the rock quickly breaks down into granular particles upon weathering. It has weathered deeply along regular joints that slice through the rock, and the outcrops become rounded because weathering is faster along the edges and corners of the joints. This combination of solid rock and deep weathering produces a rugged terrain of canyons, fins, and giant boulders, all excellent hiding places. It's no wonder Chiricahua Apache Chief Cochise used the granitic area as a refuge during the 1860s and early 1870s.

The Stronghold Granite weathers to rounded domes.

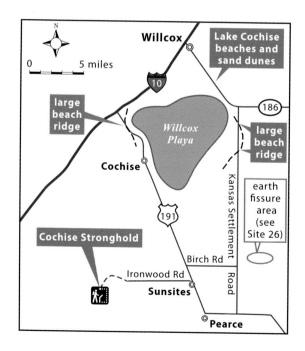

38. Willcox Playa
Remnants of Ancient Lake Cochise

Willcox Playa is a shimmering white, 40-square-mile dry lakebed in the Willcox Basin, a shallow, enclosed depression near the north end of Sulphur Springs Valley. During and immediately after the ice ages, when the climate was wetter than now, this was the deepest part of Lake Cochise. The ice-age lake was 46 feet deep and covered nearly 200 square miles. Now a few semipermanent ponds along the west and southeast shores are critical wildlife refuges that support flocks of migratory birds, especially sandhill cranes.

When the lake was completely full, one or more powerful storms washed unsorted mixtures of gravel, sand, and clay into beach ridges along the northwest and southeast lakeshores. These ridges are as much as 10 feet high and often support linear groves of mesquite trees, making the ridges obvious at a distance. US 191 travels on top of the northwest ridge about 1.5 miles south of I-10, and Kansas Settlement Road crosses the southeast ridge at 1.3 and again at 3.6 miles south of AZ 186.

As Lake Cochise receded for the last time, about 9,000 years ago, wave action along the shore formed a series of beaches that represent temporary water level stands as the lake dropped. Subdued by erosion, these terraces are difficult to see because many are covered by sand dunes composed of fine sand and silt blown from the playa by high winds. A good place to see these dunes and the old beaches is along AZ 186 near Blue Sky Road, 3.8 miles southeast of downtown Willcox.

A storm-generated beach ridge (slope at left) can be seen along US 191 on the northwest side of ancient Lake Cochise (flat plain at right).

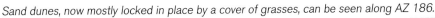

Sand dunes, now mostly locked in place by a cover of grasses, can be seen along AZ 186.

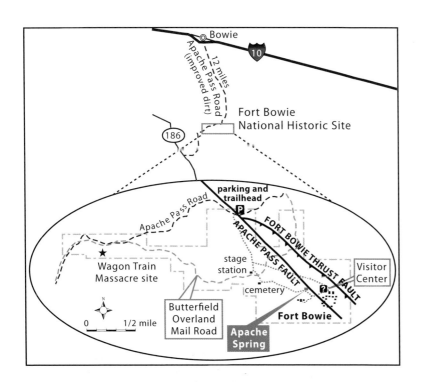

39. Fort Bowie
National Historic Site
The Dependable Water of Apache Spring

For people living in or traveling through the Southwest prior to modern times, dependable sources of water were critical. Apache Spring, with a small but reliable flow of 5 gallons per minute, is located within Apache Pass, a low point over the mountains between the San Simon River Valley and the Sulphur Springs Valley. Long a population center for Apache Indians, in the 1850s the spring became an important stop for settlers' wagon trains, the Butterfield Overland Mail, and military maneuvers. Fort Bowie, established at the spring in 1862, was the Army's base for fighting Cochise, and where Geronimo was held after his final surrender in 1886.

Apache Spring flows through a tree-lined grotto.
—Photo by Kristin Sanderson, National Park Service

The spring comes to the surface along a complex series of faults. The Apache Pass Fault, a strike-slip fault along which movement has mostly been horizontal, is more than 38 miles long. Rocks have been displaced by at least 7.5 miles. The fault is visible at the northwest end of the parking area, where the Rattlesnake Point Granodiorite (1.4 billion years old) on the west has been juxtaposed against the Glance Conglomerate (140 million years old). Between the parking lot and Fort Bowie, on the northeast side of the Apache Pass Fault and within sedimentary rocks, is a series of low-angle faults dominated by the Fort Bowie Thrust Fault. These faults formed during the compressional mountain building of the Laramide Orogeny 50 or more million years ago.

Water from rainfall and snowmelt soaks into the Chiricahua Mountains to the south and then flows through the subsurface until it reaches the fault zones. There, shattered rock acts as a dam and forces the water back to the surface. Apache Spring is the most reliable source of water for many miles around. To help preserve the natural environment and historic setting of the park, Apache Spring, the ruins of the fort, and the visitor center can only be reached via a round-trip hike of 3 miles.

The trace of the Apache Pass Fault (dashed line) follows the break in vegetation at the far side of the fort's parade ground clearing. Apache Spring is on the fault off the photo to the right. –National Park Service

The remains of the bathhouse (foreground) and other ruins at Fort Bowie. –National Park Service

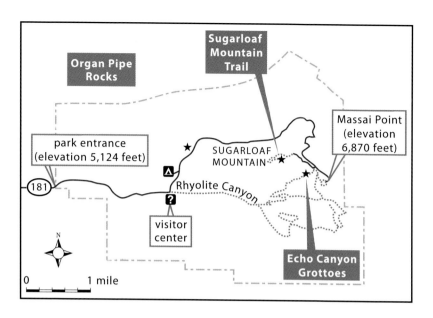

40. Chiricahua National Monument
Eroded Columns of Welded Tuff

Southern Arizona was the site of extensive igneous activity between 30 and 15 million years ago. Most of the magma bodies remained at depth where they solidified into various granitic rocks. Now and then, though, the magma approached the surface and erupted as titanic caldera volcanoes. One of these was the Turkey Creek Caldera. When it formed 27 million years ago, the crater was some 12 miles across and 5,000 feet deep. Its sequence of eruptions was probably one thousand times larger than that of Mt. St. Helens, Washington, in 1980. The countryside for miles around was blanketed with hot ash, which solidified into the Rhyolite Canyon Tuff, the rock now eroded into the rugged scenery of Chiricahua National Monument.

The Rhyolite Canyon Tuff was produced by a series of violent, gas-charged explosions of rhyolite, viscous magma rich in silica. Each explosion began with a pyroclastic flow of incandescent ash that sped across the landscape at perhaps 100 miles per hour. Often this ash was so hot that the individual particles were fused together to form a durable rock called welded tuff. Thick layers of air-fall ash were deposited on top of the flow. Another eruption produced another pyroclastic flow–ashfall sequence. There were at least three eruptions, and perhaps as many as eight. Together the layers of rhyolite ash flows and ashfalls are over 1,500 feet thick. A final eruption produced a rock with slightly less silica, called dacite. It flowed quietly across the tuff and now forms the summit of Sugarloaf Mountain, the highest point in the park. The rhyolite and dacite originally filled a valley. Since the basin-and-range uplift of the Chiricahua Mountains, erosion has stripped away surrounding rocks, leaving what had been the valley as a high point in the range, a process called inverted topography.

As the rhyolite beds cooled, they were penetrated by steam vents and broken by a series of vertical fractures called joints. Today, rain and snowmelt seep into the joints, where weathering breaks down the rock. An early stage of this process can be seen at Organ Pipe Rocks, where the joints have been deeply eroded but the columns are barely separated. Further

A light snow covers Organ Pipe Rocks, where joints are highly visible, but the rock has not yet weathered into separate columns.
—Photo by S. Hart, National Park Service

At Heart of Rocks, the tuff has weathered into separate columns. Sugarloaf Mountain is in the distance.

weathering opens the joint spaces and forms separate columns, such as at Heart of Rocks. The columns are strong, solid rock and rarely fall. Their usual demise is continued weathering. Eventually, they will just wear away.

The Massai Point Nature Trail (a partially paved 0.5-mile loop) at the end of the road provides an overlook into the Heart of Rocks. A gentle hike to the Echo Canyon Grottoes (1 mile round-trip) goes directly into slots among the columns. A longer and steeper hike up Sugarloaf Mountain (1.8 miles round-trip) features fresh cuts into the tuff where some pyroclastic flows and steam vents are exposed, and then climbs into the dacite that caps the mountain.

The columns are composed of Rhyolite Canyon Tuff, a hard volcanic rock.

41. Tombstone
Nineteenth-century Silver Mines

In 1877, prospector Ed Schieffelin headed into some hills where, he had been told, all he would find was his tombstone. He fittingly named his first mining claim Tombstone, and then in 1878 he found some richer silver deposits he called the Lucky Cuss, Good Enough, and Toughnut. Other prospectors flocked to the area and quickly located other mines. Within two years, Tombstone was one of the largest cities between the Mississippi River and San Francisco.

The geology of the Tombstone ore is complex. Put simply, 72 million years ago the Schieffelin Granodiorite intruded sedimentary rocks of Paleozoic and Cretaceous ages. Mineralizing solutions driven from the cooling magma formed the deposits, mostly within the Cretaceous rocks. Altered and enriched in more recent times, ore near the surface was extremely rich, dominated by silver chloride and lead carbonate. Assays of selected ore showed more than 300 ounces of silver per ton.

The initial boom was brief. Water was struck when the mines reached only a few hundred feet deep. Pumps were unable to keep up with the flow, and flooding combined with a depressed price of silver caused most mines to shut down before 1890. The installation of larger pumps led to a resurgence of activity in the early 1900s, but mining at Tombstone all but ended when those pumps failed in 1911. Explorations since have failed to locate any new deposit of significance. Still, the Tombstone mines produced over 30 million ounces of silver plus substantial gold, lead, copper, and zinc. Tombstone, known as "the town too tough to die," now survives on tourism. The Good Enough Mine is open for short but excellent underground tours.

The main adit of the Toughnut Mine, one of the 1878 discoveries by Ed Schieffelin.

Some silver ore was left unmined in Tombstone's Good Enough Mine.

It is said that Morgan silver dollars coined at the New Orleans mint in the early 1880s were made using Tombstone silver. This is an 1883-O coin in the author's collection.

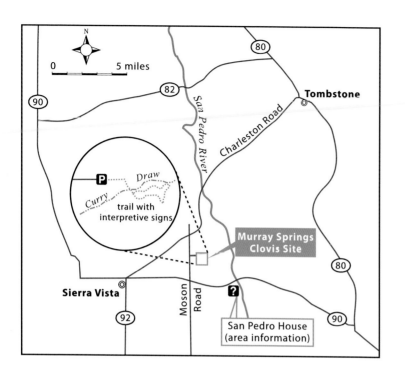

42. Murray Springs Clovis Site
Prehistoric Mammoth Hunters

Around 13,000 years ago, southern Arizona was cooler and wetter than it is today. The valleys supported plants that now grow in the mountains, streams were permanent, and animals such as Columbian mammoths, bison, giant ground sloths, and saber-toothed cats were abundant. People were here, too. The earliest well-documented human population in the Americas is called the Clovis Culture. Their artifacts, especially the famous fluted projectile points, and animal kills have been found in many North American localities. Five sites in Arizona's San Pedro Valley (Murray Springs, Escapule, Lehner Ranch, and two sites at Naco) are extremely well preserved and the first to show a clear connection between the Clovis artifacts and actual kills and butchering of mammoths and bison.

Excavations at these sites found Clovis points among mammoth and bison bones at kill sites, and skinning tools and toolmaking debris at nearby campsites. The animal

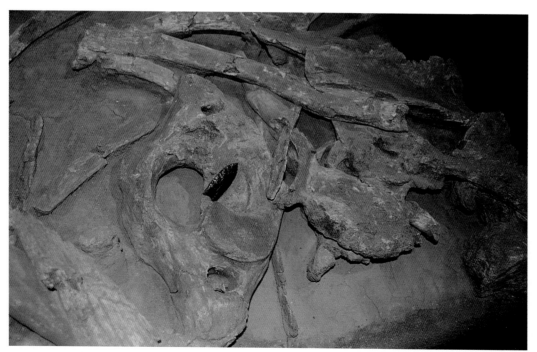

A display showing a Clovis point among mammoth bones, reconstructed in the Arizona State Museum in Tucson but as found at the Naco site in the San Pedro Valley. The point is about 3 inches long.

At the time of the Clovis Culture, Curry Draw was a wetland. Now it usually is a dry wash.

remains were found immediately below a geologic horizon known as the black mat, a layer of organic-rich clay that occurs in many places and has been dated to 12,900 years ago using radiocarbon dating. The black mat marks a time of significant climate cooling called the Younger Dryas. Some scientists have recently hypothesized that the cooling was caused by an impact between the Earth and a comet. Others disagree. Whatever its cause, the onset of the Younger Dryas 12,900 years ago marked the end of the Clovis Culture, as well as the extinction of ice-age animals such as the mammoth. People continued to live in North America but no longer made Clovis points or hunted mammoths.

Murray Springs, the only one of the San Pedro sites developed for the public, includes an improved trail with interpretive displays along Curry Draw, where the black mat is clearly exposed.

The black mat is the grayish layer halfway up the cut along the side of Curry Draw.

43. Bisbee
Queen of the Copper Camps

Mineralization was first noted at Bisbee in 1875, but it was not until 1877 that the deposits were claimed because of lead and zinc minerals. Copper was initially believed to be secondary, but it quickly became the most important metal with the opening of the Copper Queen Mine. In time, many other mines were opened, and Bisbee became Arizona's richest mining town. By the time operations ended in 1974, the mines had yielded over 8 billion pounds of copper, almost 310 million pounds of lead, and over 378 million pounds of zinc. With almost 103 million ounces of silver and over 2.7 million ounces of gold, Bisbee was Arizona's number one producer of those metals, too.

The oldest rock at Bisbee is the Pinal Schist, about 1.7 billion years old. A thick sequence of Paleozoic sedimentary rocks, most of which are limestones, was deposited on top of it. Roughly 180 million years ago, during Jurassic time, these rocks were intruded by a granite porphyry called the Sacramento Stock. The limestones were deformed by the intrusion, and fractures radiated in all directions outward from the stock. Invaded by mineralizing solutions driven from the cooling magma, limestone along the fissures was replaced by copper, lead, zinc, and silver minerals. Later, deposits near the surface were altered, leached, and enriched as groundwater percolated through the

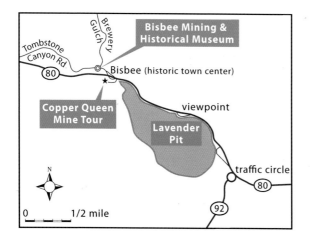

The deep hole of Bisbee's Lavender Pit mine. Acid mine drainage, water concentrated with sulfuric acid and toxic metals, seeps into the bottom.

The brilliantly colored rocks along AZ 80 were altered by the same hot fluids that deposited Bisbee's ore.

ore. This oxidized ore was often precipitated into open spaces, and the resulting minerals (at least 265 known varieties) are often spectacularly crystallized. The most famous of the rich deposits was the cylindrical Glory Hole at the Copper Queen Mine, which was 60 feet in diameter and 400 feet long. It alone produced over 20 million pounds of copper.

Ore deposits of this sort are unreliable. Rich zones may suddenly fade into barren rock. Historically, the only way to find more ore was to dig more tunnels and shafts in the hope of finding another rich shoot. As the mines went deeper, they grew less profitable, and mining gradually turned to open pits yielding large volumes of low-grade ore. The Sacramento Pit was opened in 1913 and later was incorporated into the much larger Lavender Pit. Sacramento Hill, the outcrop of the granite porphyry stock, was completely mined away. What was a hill 600 feet high is now a pit that measures 3,000 by 1,500 feet wide and 900 feet deep.

The many millions of pounds of copper deep underground might lead to renewed mining in the future. Meanwhile, AZ 80 runs along the rim of the Lavender Pit, where there is a large viewpoint. One-hour tours (reservations recommended) reach 1,500 feet into the Copper Queen Mine.

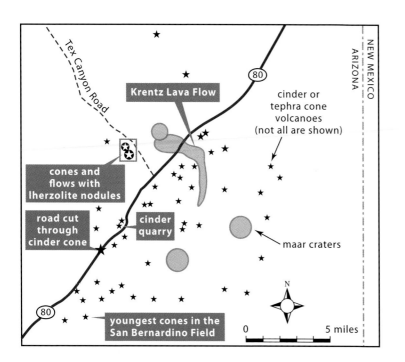

Map labels:
Tex Canyon Road
Krentz Lava Flow
cinder or tephra cone volcanoes (not all are shown)
cones and flows with lherzolite nodules
road cut through cinder cone
cinder quarry
maar craters
youngest cones in the San Bernardino Field
NEW MEXICO
ARIZONA
80
N
0   5 miles

San Bernardino nodules with yellowish brown olivine. Note the brilliant green grains of chrome diopside and the reddish brown basalt at the bottom edge. This nodule is about 3 inches wide.

44. San Bernardino Volcanic Field
Unusual Rocks from the Earth's Interior

The San Bernardino Volcanic Field includes at least 135 vents that were active between 3,300,000 and 274,000 years ago. Most of the volcanoes erupted semifluid lava that formed small spatter cones, which are cinder cones where the erupted particles of molten lava were not completely solidified before accumulating around the vent. Lava flows are limited in extent here. The field also includes five maar craters, but they are inaccessible within private ranches away from public roads.

The rock is the low-silica variety of basalt called basanite. The magma apparently formed 40 miles below the surface by a partial melting of the Earth's upper mantle at a temperature of around 2,500 degrees Fahrenheit and a pressure of 300,000 pounds per square inch. The magma rose directly to the surface, carrying chunks of unmelted mantle rock, called lherzolite, along with it. The lherzolite nodules consist mostly of yellowish brown olivine and emerald green chrome diopside minerals. They are similar to the nodules in the San Carlos Volcanic Field at Peridot Mesa (Site 19) except they contain no large gemstones of peridot and comparatively little pyroxene. Also different is that some San Bernardino lavas contain visible crystals: transparent plagioclase crystals as large as 1 inch, black crystals of pyroxene that resemble glassy obsidian, smaller but well-formed octahedral (eight-sided) crystals of spinel, and uncommon crystals of kaersutite, an amphibole mineral distinguishable by its excellent cleavage (the tendency to break along a flat surface controlled by the crystal structure).

AZ 80 cuts directly through one of the cones near milepost 391, and it crosses the flat surface of the Krentz Lava Flow, the field's longest between mileposts 398 and 399. The best place to collect lherzolite nodules and crystals is in the cliffs of two small cones on the southwest side of Tex Canyon/Rucker Canyon Road at a point 2 miles northwest of AZ 80.

Although they are mostly eroded and grass covered, every hill on the floor of the San Bernardino Valley is a volcano.

The basalt cliffs of two small cones near Tex Canyon Road contain nodules of lherzolite and crystals of uncommon minerals.

GLOSSARY

alluvial fan. The fan-shaped deposit of sediment on a valley floor at the mouth of a canyon, usually in a desert environment.

aluminum silicate. A silicate mineral in which some of the silicon atoms in the crystal structure are replaced by aluminum atoms.

amphibole. A large class of minerals of widely varying compositions but all having a double-chain silicate structure in common; the most common amphibole is the mineral hornblende.

andesite. A volcanic rock of intermediate composition, containing less iron and more silica than basalt; the silica content of andesite is typically 55 to 60 percent.

arkose. A sandstone that contains particles of feldspar minerals in addition to quartz.

badlands. A barren area of extreme erosion and little or no development of soil.

basalt. The iron- and magnesium-rich, silica-poor volcanic rock of most lava flows, and of cinder cones and shield volcanoes; the silica content of basalt is typically 45 to 50 percent.

basanite. A variety of basalt that is slightly deficient of silica; generally indistinguishable in the hand specimen from ordinary basalt but geologically significant in that it commonly is derived directly from the Earth's mantle.

breccia. A sedimentary rock composed of large, angular rock fragments held together by a fine-grained matrix of sand or silt.

calcite. The most common mineral form of calcium carbonate, $CaCO_3$.

carbonic acid. An acid (H_2CO_3) formed when carbon dioxide is dissolved in water; most groundwater is a weak carbonic acid solution, as are carbonated beverages such as soda pop.

cinder cone. A small volcanic mountain composed of loose particles of lava that were erupted and solidified in the air before accumulating as loose particles around a volcanic vent.

conglomerate. A sedimentary rock composed of large, rounded cobbles held together by a fine-grained matrix of sand or silt.

crossbeds/crossbedding. Internal bedding, or layers, in sedimentary rock that are angled with respect to the rock layer, caused by the movement of sedimentary particles by wind or water.

dacite. A volcanic rock of intermediate composition between rhyolite and andesite; chemically equivalent to the intrusive rock granodiorite.

debris flow. A flood composed mostly of mud and rock, and as little as 20 percent water, that can move huge boulders out of mountain canyons with great destructive momentum.

detachment fault. A low-angle fault that separates a lower plate suite of metamorphic rocks below the fault, usually exposed as a metamorphic core complex, from an upper plate of broken rocks that commonly have been moved many miles from their point of origin.

diatreme. A volcanic vent formed by an explosive eruption. The cone-shaped subsurface vent is filled with broken rock and lava and commonly capped by a maar crater.

diopside. A member of the pyroxene group of minerals, in pure form $CaMgSi_2O_6$; a variety that contains chromium is a common constituent of lherzolite.

feldspar. A group of silicate minerals, either orthoclase (potassium feldspar) or plagioclase (sodium-calcium feldspar), that are components of many kinds of rock.

floodplain. An open, level area along a stream or river that is occasionally flooded, receiving silty and sandy sedimentary deposits.

formation. A rock unit that can be readily distinguished from other rock units on the basis of color, composition, fossil content, and so on; commonly given a formal name such as Schnebly Hill Formation.

gneiss. A metamorphic rock formed under high-temperature and high-pressure conditions that result in a banded appearance of alternating light and dark colored minerals.

granite. A silica-rich intrusive igneous rock composed mostly of quartz and orthoclase feldspar plus lesser amounts of plagioclase feldspar and mica minerals.

granitic rock. A catchall term for intrusive igneous rocks that are relatively rich in silica and poor in iron and magnesium, including syenite, granite, and granodiorite.

granodiorite. An intrusive igneous rock of intermediate composition, composed mostly of orthoclase and plagioclase feldspars, plus lesser amounts of quartz, amphibole, and mica.

igneous. Rocks formed from cooled and crystallized magma; intrusive igneous rocks form at depth below the Earth's surface while extrusive, or volcanic, igneous rocks form from lava on the Earth's surface.

inverted topography. A ridge or mountain that once was low land but now is elevated above its surroundings because of a resistance to erosion.

joints. Fractures that cut through otherwise solid rock, often forming three-dimensional, cube-like frameworks along which weathering takes place.

lava. Molten rock erupted by a volcano onto the Earth's surface; see magma.

lherzolite. A rock composed predominately of olivine associated with diopside, pyroxene, and spinel that represents fragments of the Earth's mantle brought to the surface by volcanic eruptions; usually found as nodules within basanite lava flows.

maar. A wide, shallow crater that forms during the explosive eruption of a diatreme.

magma. Molten rock confined at depth below the Earth's surface; see lava.

meander. A wide, curving bend in a river.

megabreccia. A chaotic mixture of unsorted rock fragments of extremely large size, sometimes reaching several hundred feet in dimension.

member. A subdivision within a formally named rock formation; for example, the limestone Fort Apache Member of the mostly sandstone Schnebly Hill Formation.

metamorphic. From *meta* ("change") and *morph* ("shape"), the recrystallization of an existing rock into a new form because of changing temperature and/or pressure conditions.

metamorphic core complex. A geologic structure in which a core of deep-seated metamorphic rock is exposed when overlying rocks are removed along a detachment fault.

mineralizing solution. The fluid, composed mostly of water but also containing carbon dioxide, hydrogen sulfide, metals, and other dissolved ions, that is driven from a cooling magma into surrounding rocks.

Mogollon Rim. Extending from northwest to southeast across Arizona and into New Mexico, it is a prominent escarpment that serves as the geologic boundary between the Colorado Plateau and Transition Zone provinces. Usually pronounced "muggy-own," it is named after Don Juan Ignacio Flores Mogollón, Spanish colonial governor of New Mexico in 1712–1715.

normal fault. A fault that cuts through the crust at a high angle, along which the rocks beneath the fault have been moved upwards; common to regions where the crust has been stretched, such as in the Basin and Range Province.

olivine. A magnesium-iron silicate mineral, $(Mg,Fe)_2SiO_4$, common in low-silica rocks such as basalt; called peridot when of gem quality.

orogeny. From Greek *oro* ("mountain") and *geny* ("genesis"), an episode of mountain building.

orthoclase. A variety of feldspar, potassium-aluminum silicate, $KAlSi_3O_8$.

peridot. The gem-quality form of the mineral olivine.

plagioclase. A variety of feldspar, sodium-calcium aluminum silicate, $(Na,Ca)(Al,Si)_4O_8$.

pluton. A body of intrusive igneous rock, such as granite, formed at depth below the Earth's surface.

porphyry. The textural term for an igneous rock that contains distinct mineral crystals disseminated throughout the rock.

Precambrian. An informal but handy time unit that represents the first 86 percent of Earth history, from 4.6 billion up to 542 million years ago; in formal geology, comprised of the Hadean, Archean, and Proterozoic eons.

pyroclastic. From Greek *pyro* ("fire") and *klastos* ("broken"), shattered rock fragments, such as ash and cinders, produced by explosive volcanic eruptions.

pyroxene. A large class of minerals of widely varying compositions but all having a single-chain silicate structure in common; the most common pyroxene is the mineral augite, essentially a calcium-iron-magnesium aluminum silicate.

quartz. The single most common mineral on Earth, pure silicon dioxide, SiO_2.

rhyolite. The iron- and magnesium-poor, silica-rich volcanic rock typical of explosive volcanic eruptions, including calderas; the silica content of rhyolite is usually greater than 68 percent.

sand dune. An accumulation of windblown sand.

sandstone. The sedimentary rock composed of sand-sized particles bonded together into solid rock.

silica. The pure dioxide of silicon, SiO_2, most commonly found as the mineral quartz.

silicate. The class of minerals where the fundamental building blocks of the crystal structures are pyramids composed of one silicon atom surrounded by four oxygen atoms, SiO_4, that are linked together into various chains, sheets, and other networks. About one-half of all minerals are silicates.

sinkhole. A surface depression formed by an inward collapse in the subsurface, often a limestone cavern.

spinel. In pure form, a magnesium aluminum oxide mineral, $MgAl_2O_4$, but sharing a crystal structure with several other minerals so that it may contain chemical elements such as iron and chromium.

stalactite. The variety of large cave formation that hangs down from the roof of a limestone cavern.

stalagmite. The variety of large cave formation that grows upward from the floor of a limestone cavern. When a stalactite and stalagmite merge into a single structure, it is called a column.

stock. A pluton of relatively small size, by one definition having an exposed surface area of less than 40 square miles.

subduction. An episode of plate tectonics in which a plate of oceanic crust is forced downward beneath some other plate of crust, which may be either oceanic or continental.

thrust fault. A low-angle fault on which compression or squeezing of the crust has caused the material above the fault to be moved up and over the material below the fault.

tuff. The rock composed of volcanic ash and other fragmented materials produced by explosive volcanic eruptions; see welded tuff.

unconformity. A gap, or interruption, in the rock record, representing a time span when sedimentary rocks either did not form at all or did form but were eroded away before deposition was renewed.

volcanic neck. The subsurface conduit, or pipe, of an extinct volcano, now exposed by erosion that has removed the volcano's cone and surrounding materials.

welded tuff. Volcanic ash in which individual rock particles were fused, or welded, together by high temperatures to form a solid rock.

zeolite. A large family of silicate minerals within which there are molecular channels large enough to absorb other chemical compounds, which makes some zeolites valuable as chemical filters.

ONLINE SITE INFORMATION

Prior to visiting each location, it is recommended you check for current conditions, hours of operation, and possible closures due to wildfires, rock slides, or other potential hazards. Many of the Web sites listed below also include geologic information.

Several sites (9. Pinta Dome, 10. Hopi Buttes, 18. Malpais Hill Zeolites, 22. Bouse Formation, 44. San Bernardino Volcanic Field) do not have Web sites either dedicated to them or encompassing them.

1. Lees Ferry
http://www.nps.gov/glca/planyourvisit/cathedralwashhike.htm
http://www.nps.gov/glca/planyourvisit/lees-ferry.htm

2. Horseshoe Bend
http://www.nps.gov/glca/

3. Tuba City dinosaur tracks
http://www.navajonationparks.org/parks.htm

4. Grand Canyon Trail of Time
http://tot.unm.edu/
http://www.nps.gov/grca

5. Sunset Crater Volcano National Monument
http://www.nps.gov/sucr

6. Wupatki National Monument
http://www.nps.gov/wupa/naturescience/geology_overview.htm

7. Barringer Meteorite Crater
http://www.meteorcrater.com
http://www.barringercrater.com

8. Petrified Forest National Park
http://www.nps.gov/pefo

11. Canyon de Chelly National Monument
http://www.nps.gov/cach

12. Monument Valley
http://monumentvalley.org/geology/
http://www.navajonationparks.org/htm/monumentvalley.htm

13. Sedona red rocks
http://www.fs.usda.gov/main/coconino
http://www.redrockscenicbyway.com

14. Granite Dells
http://www.cityofprescott.net/services/parks/parks

15. Montezuma Well
http://www.nps.gov/moca/montezuma-well.htm

16. Tonto Natural Bridge State Park
http://www.azstateparks.com/Parks/tona/science

17. Superstition Mountain Caldera
http://www.fs.fed.us/r3/tonto

19. Peridot Mesa
http://www.sancarlosapache.com/San_Carlos_Culture_Center.htm

20. Morenci Mine
http://www.fcx.com/operations/USA_Arizona_Morenci.htm

21. Peach Spring Tuff
http://www.cityofkingman.gov/pages/depts/parks/walking.asp

23. Vulture Mountains and Mine
http://www.jcp-training.com/vulture.htm

24. Burro Creek Canyon
http://www.blm.gov/az/st/en/prog/recreation/camping/dev_camps/burrocr.html

25. Papago Park and Camelback Mountain
http://www.arizona-vacation-planner.com/
  camelback-mountain.html
http://phoenix.gov/PARKS/hikcfac.html

26. Earth Fissures
http://www.azgs.az.gov/EFC.shtml

27. Picacho Peak State Park
http://www.azstateparks.com/Parks/PIPE

28. Sentinel Plain Volcanic Field
http://www.blm.gov/az/st/en/prog/recreation/autotour/
  agua.html

29. Saguaro National Park, East
http://www.nps.gov/sagu

30. Catalina State Park
http://azstateparks.com/Parks/CATA

31. Saguaro National Park, West
http://www.nps.gov/sagu
http://www.pima.gov/nrpr/parks/tmp

32. University of Arizona Mineral Museum
http://www.flandrau.org
http://www.uamineralmuseum.org

33. Mineral Discovery Center at Mission Mine
http://www.mineraldiscovery.com

34. Kitt Peak
http://www.noao.edu/kpno/

35. Organ Pipe Cactus National Monument
http://www.nps.gov/orpi

36. Kartchner Caverns State Park
http://azstateparks.com/Parks/KACA

37. Cochise Stronghold
http://www.fs.fed.us/r3/Coronado/CochiseStronghold.shtml
http://www.cochisestronghold.com

38. Willcox Playa
http://www.azheritagewaters.nau.edu/loc_wilcox_playa.html
http://www.azgfd.gov/outdoor_recreation/wildlife_area_
  wilcox_playa.shtml

39. Fort Bowie National Historic Site
http://www.nps.gov/fobo

40. Chiricahua National Monument
http://www.nps.gov/chir

41. Tombstone
http://www.cityoftombstone.com/

42. Murray Springs Clovis Site
http://www.blm.gov/az/st/en/prog/cultural/murray.html

43. Bisbee
http://www.bisbeemuseum.org
http://www.queenminetour.com

ADDITIONAL WEB SITES WITH GEOLOGICAL AND TRAVEL INFORMATION

http://arizonahiking.blogspot.com

http://www.arizona-vacation-planner.com

http://www.hikearizona.com

http://www.azgs.az.gov

http://azgeology.azgs.az.gov

http://www.azheritagewaters.nau.edu

http://geomaps.wr.usgs.gov/parks

http://www.arizonageologicalsoc.org

REFERENCES

GENERAL SOURCES

Abbott, L., and T. Cook. 2007. *Geology Underfoot in Northern Arizona*. Missoula, MT: Mountain Press Publishing Company.

Anthony, J. W., S. A. Williams, W. E. Wilson, and R. W. Grant. 1995. *Mineralogy of Arizona*. Tucson: University of Arizona Press.

Arizona State Parks. 2008. *A Brief Overview of the Cultural History of Arizona*. Arizona Site Steward Program.

Bearce, N. R. 2004. *Minerals of Arizona: A Field Guide for Collectors*. Tempe, AZ: Arizona Desert Ice Press.

Chronic, H. 1983. *Roadside Geology of Arizona*. Missoula, MT: Mountain Press Publishing Company.

Fellows, L. D. 2000. Volcanism in Arizona. *Arizona Geology* 30:4.

Jenney, J. P., and S. J. Reynolds, eds. 1989. *Geologic Evolution of Arizona*. Arizona Geological Society Digest 17.

Lucchitta, I. 2001. *Hiking Arizona's Geology*. Seattle, WA: The Mountaineers Books.

Names Committee. 2010. *Divisions of Geologic Time—Major Chronostratigraphic and Geochronologic Units*. U.S. Geological Survey Fact Sheet 2010–3059 (July 2010).

Nations, D., and E. Stump. 1996. *Geology of Arizona*. Dubuque, IA: Kendall-Hunt Publishing Company.

Peirce, H. W. 1969. *Map and Cross-Sections of Arizona*. Arizona Geological Survey Map 14.

Reynolds, S. J. 1989. *Geologic Map of Arizona*. Arizona Geological Survey Map 26.

Walker, J. D., and J. W. Geissman, compilers. 2009. *Geologic Time Scale*. Geological Society of America, as reported by the International Commission on Stratigraphy.

SPECIFIC SOURCES

Allen, R. 2003. Rock and roll geology. *Northwest Valley Lifestyles Magazine*, August 2003.

Allen, R. 2004. Missing time. *Northwest Valley Lifestyles Magazine*, January 2004.

Amann, A. W., Jr., J. V. Bezy, R. Ratkevich, and W. M. Witkind. 1997. *Ice Age Mammals of the San Pedro River Valley, Southeastern Arizona*. Arizona Geological Survey Down-to-Earth 6.

Arizona Geological Survey. 2009. *Earth Fissures Map of the Signal Peak Study Area, Pinal County, Arizona*. Arizona Geological Survey Earth Fissures Map 6 (DM-EF-6).

Arizona Geological Survey. 2009. *Earth Fissures Map of the Toltec Buttes Study Area, Pinal County, Arizona*. Arizona Geological Survey Earth Fissures Map 8 (DM-EF-8).

Bailey, L. R. 1983. *Bisbee: Queen of the Copper Camps*. Tucson, AZ: Westernlore Press.

Bailey, L. R. 2010. *Too Tough to Die: The Rise, Fall, and Resurrection of a Silver Camp, 1878 to 1990*. Tucson, AZ: Westernlore Press.

Bezy, J. V. 2001. *Rocks in the Chiricahua National Monument and the Fort Bowie National Historic Site*. Arizona Geological Survey Down-to-Earth 11.

Bezy, J. V. 2002. *A Guide to the Geology of Catalina State Park and the Western Santa Catalina Mountains*. Arizona Geological Survey Down-to-Earth 12.

Bezy, J. V. 2002. *A Guide to the Geology of Sabino Canyon and the Catalina Highway*. Arizona Geological Survey Down-to-Earth 17.

Bezy, J. V. 2005. *A Guide to the Geology of Saguaro National Park*. Arizona Geological Survey Down-to-Earth 18.

Bezy, J. V., J. T. Gutmann, and G. B. Haxel. 2000. *A Guide to the Geology of Organ Pipe Cactus National Monument and the Pinacate Biosphere Reserve*. Arizona Geological Survey Down-to-Earth 9.

Bezy, J. V., and A. S. Trevena. 2000. *Guide to Geologic Features at Petrified Forest National Park*. Arizona Geological Survey Down-to-Earth 10.

Blakey, R. C., and L. T. Middleton. 1987. Late Paleozoic Depositional systems, Sedona-Jerome area, central Arizona. In *Geologic Diversity of Arizona and Its Margins: Excursions to Choice Areas*. Arizona Bureau of Geology and Mineral Technology Special Paper 5, editors. G. H. Davis and E. M. VandenDolder, 143–57.

Bureau of Land Management. 2000. Sentinel Plain. In *Barry M. Goldwater Range Non-Renewed Parcels Study*, in compliance with the Military Lands Withdrawal Act of 1999 (Public Law 106-65), 20–21.

Cave, S. R., R. Greeley, D. E. Champion, and B. D. Turrin. 2007. *40Ar/39Ar Ages for the Sentinel-Arlington Volcanic Field, Southwestern Arizona*. American Geophysical Union, Fall Meeting (San Francisco). Abstract V23B-1439.

Chenoweth, W. L. 2000. Road log of Monument Valley Navajo Tribal Park, Utah and Arizona. In *Geologic Road, Trail and Lake Guides to Utah's Parks and Monuments*. Utah Geological Association Publication 29, P. B. Anderson and D. A. Sprinkel, editors.

Clemons, R. E., and H. L. James. 1978. Supplemental road log No. 4: Willcox to Bowie. In *Land of Cochise*. New Mexico Geological Society 29th Field Conference Guidebook, H. L. James, managing editor, 125–38.

Devere, B. J., Jr. 1978. The Tombstone Mining District—History, geology and ore deposits. In *Land of Cochise*. New Mexico Geological Society 29th Field Conference Guidebook, H. L. James, managing editor, 315–20.

Diaz, M. undated. *Geologic Mysteries—Tonto Natural Bridge*. Arizona Geological Survey brochure.

DiChristina, M. 2010. The coming shortage of helium. *Scientific American*, http://blogs.scientificamerican.com/observations.

Drewes, H. 1977. Geologic map and sections of the Rincon Valley quadrangle. U.S. Geological Survey Miscellaneous Investigations Series Map I-997.

Duffield, W. A. 1997. *Volcanoes of Northern Arizona: Sleeping Giants of the Grand Canyon Region*. Grand Canyon, AZ: Grand Canyon Association.

Fellows, L. D. 2001. Chiricahua Monument and Fort Bowie. *Arizona Geology* 31(3):1–2.

Ferguson, C. A. 2008. Silver Creek Caldera, probable source of the Miocene Peach Spring Tuff, Oatman Mining District, Arizona. Geological Society of America *Abstracts with Programs* 40:33.

Frey, F. A., and M. Prinz. 1971. Ultramafic nodules from San Carlos, Arizona. Geological Society of America *Abstracts with Programs* 3.

Gelt, J. 1992. Land subsidence, earth fissures change Arizona's landscape. University of Arizona, Water Resources Research Center. *Arroyo* 6(2):1–12.

Gray, F., et al. 1985. *Geologic Map of the Growler Mountains, Pima and Maricopa Counties, Arizona*. U.S. Geological Survey Miscellaneous Field Studies (Map MF-1681).

Hanson, S. 2009. Sunset Crater Volcano. *Arizona Geology* 37:1.

Hayes, C. V., Jr., and B. B. Huckell, eds. 2007. *Murray Springs: A Clovis Site with Multiple Activity Areas in the San Pedro Valley, Arizona*. University of Arizona Anthropological Paper Number 71.

Hellmich-Bryan, J. 2011. Personal communication, Chief of Interpretation and Resource Education, Grand Canyon National Park.

Hill, C. A. 1999. Mineralogy of Kartchner Caverns, Arizona. *Journal of Cave and Karst Studies* 61(2):73–78.

Houk, R. 2005. *The Guide to National Parks of the Southwest*, 82-83. Tucson: Western National Parks Association.

Karlstrom, K., et al. 2008. Informal geoscience education on a grand scale: The Trail of Time exhibition at Grand Canyon. *Journal of Geoscience Education* 56(4):354–61.

Keith, S. B. 1978. First day road log from Lordsburg to Douglas. In *Land of Cochise*. New Mexico Geological Society 29th

Field Conference Guidebook, H. L. James, managing editor, 1–30.

KellerLynn, K. 2010. *Petrified Forest National Park: Geologic Resources Inventory Report.* Natural Resource Report NPS/NRPC/GRD/NRR–2010/218. Fort Collins, CO: National Park Service.

King, M. 2011. Personal communication, Chief of Interpretation, Glen Canyon National Recreation Area.

Kring, D. A., ed. 2002. *Desert Heat—Volcanic Fire: The Geologic History of the Tucson Mountains and Southern Arizona.* Arizona Geological Society Digest 21.

Kring, D. A. 2007. *Guidebook to the Geology of Barringer Meteorite Crater, Arizona.* Lunar and Planetary Institute Contribution No. 1355.

Lipman, P. W. 1993. *Geological Map of the Tucson Mountains Caldera, Southern Arizona.* U.S. Geological Survey Miscellaneous Investigations Series Map I-2205.

Lockley, M. G., and A. P. Hunt. 1995. *Dinosaur Tracks and Other Footprints of the Western United States.* New York: Columbia University Press.

Long, K. R. 1995. Production and reserves of Cordilleran (Alaska to Chile) porphyry copper deposits in Arizona. In *Porphyry Copper Deposits in the American Cordillera,* Arizona Geological Society Digest 20, F. W. Pierce and J. G. Bolm, editors, 35–68.

Lucas, S. G., C. Lewis, W. R. Dickinson, and A. B. Heckert. 2005. The late Cretaceous Tucson Mountains dinosaur. In *Vertebrate Paleontology in Arizona.* New Mexico Museum of Natural History and Science Bulletin 29, A. B. Heckert and S. G. Lucas, editors, 111–13.

Lucchitta, I. 1972. Early history of the Colorado River in the Basin and Range Province [abstract]. Geological Society of America *Bulletin* 83(7):1933.

Lucchitta, I., R. F. Holm, and B. K. Lucchitta. 2011. A Miocene river in northern Arizona and its implications for the Colorado River and Grand Canyon. *GSA Today* 21(10):4–10.

Lynch, D. J. 1978. The San Bernardino Volcanic Field of southeastern Arizona. In *Land of Cochise.* New Mexico Geological Society 29th Field Conference Guidebook, H. L. James, managing editor, 261–68.

Lynch, D. J. 1989. Neogene volcanism in Arizona: The recognizable volcanoes. In *Geologic Evolution of Arizona.* Arizona Geological Society Digest 17, J. P. Jenney and S. J. Reynolds, editors, 681–700.

Martin, P. S. 1963. Geochronology of pluvial Lake Cochise, southern Arizona. *Ecology* 44(3):436–44.

Marvin, R. F., C. W. Naeser, and H. H. Mehnert. 1978. Tabulation of radiometric ages—including unpublished K-Ar and fission-track ages—for rocks in southeastern Arizona and southwestern New Mexico. In *Land of Cochise.* New Mexico Geological Society 29th Field Conference Guidebook, H. L. James, managing editor, 243–52.

Meek, N., and J. Douglass. 2001. Lake overflow: An alternative hypothesis for Grand Canyon incision and development of the Colorado River. In *The Colorado River: Origin and Evolution, Grand Canyon, Arizona.* Grand Canyon Association Monograph 12, R. A. Young and E. E. Spammer, editors, 199–204.

National Optical Astronomy Observatory. 2008. *Kitt Peak Docent Training Manual 2008.* Available online at www.noao.edu/outreach/kpvc/docent-news/training-2008.pdf.

National Park Service. 2006. *Geologic Resource Evaluation Scoping Summary, Fort Bowie National Historic Site, Arizona.* Geologic Resources Division, National Park Service.

National Park Service. undated. *Wupatki Pueblo Trail Guide.* Western National Parks Association.

Nations, J. D., R. H Hevly, D. W. Blinn, and J. J. Landye. 1981. Paleontology, paleoecology, and depositional history of the Miocene-Pliocene Verde Formation, Yavapai County, Arizona. *Arizona Geological Society Digest* 13:133–49.

Nealey, L. D., and M. F. Sheridan. 1989. Post-Laramide volcanic rocks of Arizona and northern Sonora, Mexico, and their inclusions. In *Geologic Evolution of Arizona.* Arizona Geological Society Digest 17, J. P. Jenney and S. J. Reynolds, editors, 609–47.

Pallister, J. S., E. A. du Bray, and D. B. Hall. 1993. *Geology of Chiricahua National Monument, a Review for the Non-Specialist.* U.S. Geological Survey Open-File Report 93–617.

Pallister, J. S., E. A. du Bray, and D. B. Hall. 1997. *Interpretive Map and Guide to the Volcanic Geology of Chiricahua National Monument and Vicinity, Cochise County, Arizona.* U.S. Geological Survey Miscellaneous Investigations Series Map I–2541.

Pamukcu, A. S. 2010. The Evolution of the Peach Spring Tuff magmatic system revealed by accessory mineral textures and compositions. Vanderbilt University Master of Science Thesis.

Pearthree, P. A., C. A. Ferguson, B. J. Johnson, and J. Guynn. 2008. *Geologic Map and Report for the Proposed State Route 95 Realignment Corridor in Eastern Mohave Valley, Mohave County, Arizona.* Arizona Geological Survey Digital Geologic Map DGM-65.

Peirce, H. W. 1975. *Geologic Guidebook 2–Highways of Arizona: Arizona Highways 77 and 177.* Arizona Bureau of Mines Bulletin 176.

Phoenix, D. A. 1963. *Geology of the Lees Ferry Area, Coconino County, Arizona.* U.S. Geological Survey Bulletin 1137.

Priznar, N. M. 2004. *A Few Mine Related Considerations for an Enhancement of SR 80, Near Bisbee Arizona.* Arizona Department of Transportation.

Ranney, W. 2001. *Sedona Through Time.* Zia Interpretive Services.

Ranney, W. 2010. The new Trail of Time at Grand Canyon National Park–a review. *Arizona Geology* 40:1.

Rauzi, S. L., and L. D. Fellows. 2003. Arizona has helium. *Arizona Geology* 33(4).

Reynolds, S. A., and R. D. Bartlett. 2002. *Subsurface Geology of the Easternmost Phoenix Basin, Arizona: Implications for Groundwater Flow.* Arizona Geological Survey Contributed Report CR-02-A.

Reynolds, S. A., E. A. Scot, and R. T. O'Haire. 1985. A fluorite-bearing granite, Belmont Mountains, central Arizona. Arizona Geological Survey *Fieldnotes* 15(1):4–5.

Reynolds, S. J., J. E. Spencer, E. DeWitt, D. C. White, and M. J. Grubensky. 1988. *Geologic Map of the Vulture Mine Area, Vulture Mountains, West-central Arizona.* Arizona Geological Survey Open-File Report 88-10.

Risley, R. 1987. Sedimentation and stratigraphy of the lower Cretaceous Amole Arkose, Tucson Mountains, Arizona. In *Mesozoic Rocks of Southern Arizona and Adjacent Areas.* Arizona Geological Society Digest 18, W. R. Dickinson and M. A. Klute, editors, 215–28.

Schreiber, J. F. 1978. Geology of the Willcox Playa, Cochise County, Arizona. In *Land of Cochise.* New Mexico Geological Society 29th Field Conference Guidebook, H. L. James, managing editor, p. 277–82.

Shafiqullah, M., P. E. Damon, D. J. Lynch, P. H. Kuck, and W. A. Rehrig. 1978. Mid-Tertiary magmatism in southeastern Arizona. In *Land of Cochise.* New Mexico Geological Society 29th Field Conference Guidebook, H. L. James, managing editor, 231–42.

Sheridan, M. F. 1978. The Superstition Cauldron Complex. In *Guidebook to the Geology of Central Arizona.* Arizona Bureau of Geology and Mineral Technology Special Paper 2, D. M. Burt and T. L. Péwe, editors, 85–96.

Spencer, J. E., and P. A. Pearthree. 2005. Abrupt initiation of the Colorado River and initial incision of the Grand Canyon. *Arizona Geology* 35:4.

Spencer, J. E, S. J. Reynolds, M. J. Grubensky, J. T. Duncan, and D. C. White. 1989. Geology of the Vulture Gold Mine. *Arizona Geology* 19:4.

Thomssen, R. 1983. The minerals of the Malpais Hills, Pinal County, Arizona. *Mineralogical Record* 14:109–13.

Timmer, J. 2010. Price shocks waiting as US abandons helium business. *Arstechnica.com.*

Titley, S. R., and E. Y. Anthony. 1989. Laramide mineral deposits in Arizona. In *Geologic Evolution of Arizona.* Arizona Geological Society Digest 17, J. P. Jenney and S. J. Reynolds, editors, 491–500.

Toner, M. 2010. The Clovis comet controversy. *American Archaeology* 14(3):12–18.

Tosdal, R. M. 1989. Jurassic geology of the Sonoran Desert region. In *Geologic Evolution of Arizona.* Arizona Geological Society Digest 17, J. P. Jenney and S. J. Reynolds, editors, 397–434.

Tosdal, R. M., G. B. Haxel, T. H. Anderson, C. D. Connors, D. J. May, and J. E. Wright. 1990. Highlights of Jurassic, late Cretaceous to early Tertiary, and middle Tertiary tectonics, south-central Arizona and north-central Sonora. In *Geologic Excursions through the Sonoran Desert Region, Arizona and Sonora.* Geological Society of America, Cordilleran Section 86th Annual Meeting field trip guidebook, G. E. Gehrels and J. E. Spencer, editors, 76–88.

U.S. Geological Survey. 2011. *Mineral Commodity Summaries 2011.* U.S. Geological Survey.

Vanderford, R. undated. *Montezuma Well—A Natural Oasis.* National Park Service brochure.

Varney, P. 1994. *Arizona Ghost Towns and Mining Camps.* Arizona Highways Books, Arizona Department of Transportation, p. 24–27.

Ward, M. K. 2007. *So, Why Are the Rocks Red?* Mesa, AZ: Nueva Science Press.

White, J. D. L. 1991. Maar-diatreme phreatomagmatism at Hopi Buttes, Navajo Nation (Arizona), USA. *Bulletin of Volcanology* 53:239–58.

Wise, W. S., and R. W. Tschernich. 1976. The chemical composition and origin of the zeolites offretite, erionite, and levyne. *American Mineralogist* 61:853–63.

Witchalls, C. 2010. From cryogenics to MRI machines, helium is irreplaceable. *New Scientist* 207(2773):29.

Wohletz, K. H. 1978. The eruptive mechanism of the Peridot Mesa Vent, San Carlos, Arizona. In *Guidebook to the Geology of Central Arizona.* Arizona Bureau of Geology and Mineral Technology Special Paper No. 2, D. M. Burt and T. L. Pewe, editors.

Zelawski, M. 2010. The Hopi Buttes Volcanic Field, Navajo Nation, Arizona. *Arizona Geology* 40:1.

Zorich, Z. 2011. Undiscovery of the year: Cloviscomet. *Archaeology* 64(1):30.

INDEX

T. Scott Bryan and his wife, Betty Tucker-Bryan. –Photo by Toni LaPorte

About the Author

T. Scott Bryan received a B.S. in geology at San Diego State University (1972) and an M.S. at the University of Montana (1974). He worked for the National Park Service as a mining geologist in Death Valley National Monument and also held positions with Glacier National Park, Glen Canyon National Recreation Area, Los Angeles Field Office, and Yellowstone National Park. He is retired from Victor Valley Community College in Victorville, California, as emeritus professor of geology, astronomy, and physical science, and as director of the college planetarium. Scott is a member of the Geological Society of America and the Arizona Geological Society. He is the author of *The Geysers of Yellowstone* and coauthor with wife, Betty Tucker-Bryan, of *The Explorer's Guide to Death Valley National Park*, both published by the University Press of Colorado, and *Geysers: What They Are and How They Work*, published by Mountain Press Publishing Company. He has also written several magazine articles on the history and geology of the American West.